A
HANDBOOK OF
BEEKEEPING

A
HANDBOOK OF
BEEKEEPING

by

H.R.C. RICHES, M.D, F.R.C.P.

President, Central Association of Beekeepers
Past President, British Beekeepers Association

NORTHERN BEE BOOKS

First published in the U.K. in 1992 by Northern Bee Books,
Scout Bottom Farm, Mytholmroyd,
Hebden Bridge, West Yorkshire HX7 5JS

Copyright © Dr. H.R.C. Riches, M.D., F.R.C.P.

Designed by Karen Sutcliffe

Cover Design by G Fielding

Printed by Arc & Throstle Press, Nanholme Mill, Shaw Wood
Road, Todmorden. OL14 6DA

ISBN 0 907908 62 4

Oilseed Rape in full flower

Honeybee foraging on Limnanthes douglasii

CONTENTS

PHOTOGRAPHS & ILLUSTRATIONS

PREFACE

This new book attempts to describe concisely the basic essentials of practical beekeeping. Perhaps, in so doing, it may also promote greater awareness of the fascination, satisfaction, and environmental benefits of apiculture. Sadly, potential newcomers to the craft are often confused and discouraged by the multiplicity of conflicting opinions expressed about beekeeping fundamentals by 'old hands'. Methods of management; the best variety of bees; the best type of hive etc. etc. are all subjects debated *ad nauseam* by established beekeepers, usually with considerable conviction and enthusiasm. The arguments are, however, of little help to the beginner; in fact, they are counter productive in that they make the craft appear too difficult. The advice given in the following pages will, therefore, be that which is most widely accepted. Controversial minority views will be avoided.

Although much can be learnt from books and magazines, the essential first step for anyone contemplating beekeeping is to join the local Beekeepers' Association. This will give the opportunity to talk to and learn from those with practical experience. Furthermore, many associations have their own apiaries where beginners can learn the elementary principles of beekeeping and also establish that they are temperamentally suited to handling bees and not upset by the occasional sting!

It must be emphasized that it would be most unwise for a beginner to buy equipment without proper advice and without first gaining a little insight into the practical aspects of the craft. Many have spent money which they subsequently regretted. Far better to delay a little and start correctly.

Public libraries are most helpful sources of information in that they will make available on loan many of the standard textbooks on beekeeping. A recommended reading list is given at the end of this book together with the names and addresses of appropriate journals. In addition, the addresses of some important beekeeping organizations are attached.

Harry Riches
Northwood,
Middlesex.

ACKNOWLEDGEMENTS

I am grateful to my friend Robert Creighton for reading the manuscript and for making helpful suggestions which have undoubtedly improved my text. Robert has a vast experience and knowledge of beekeeping and I consider myself extremely fortunate that he so generously gave me some of his valuable time.

I am indebted to the International Bee Research Association and J.W. White Esq., author of the original publication in 'Bee World', for permission to reproduce the diagram showing how HMF increases in honey with prolonged exposure to heat.

I also wish to thank the Controller, H.M. Stationery Office for allowing me to use the photographs of honeybee brood diseases which were published in M.A.F.F. Bulletin 100 - 'Diseases of Bees'.

INTRODUCTION

I t is difficult to appreciate that honeybees were on this planet collecting nectar and pollen from flowers, and storing honey, many millions of years before primitive man emerged. After learning the value of honey as a food, our early ancestors sought to satisfy their appetites by robbing the nests of any colonies that could be found. By actively searching for nests to plunder, man became a honey hunter and continued as such for millions of years. Not until the early Egyptian civilizations are there records of bees being managed in hives. Since that time the craft of beekeeping has slowly evolved. Today, although the honeybee retains a place of special esteem for the honey and wax it produces, it is also recognized that it makes an important economic contribution in developed countries by its pollinating function. The latter benefits not only food crops but also wild plants, trees and shrubs which add so much to the amenity of our environment.

Because our changeable north European oceanic climate does not favour large scale commercial beekeeping, the craft here is largely an amateur pursuit.

Approximately 99% of U.K. beekeepers are hobbyists, or side-liners, who together own nearly 80% of all bee stocks. There are no accurate statistics relating to honey production in the British Isles but estimates are usually in the modest range of 1000 to 3000 tonnes annually. The inevitable conclusion from these few facts is that it would be foolish to expect to make a fortune from beekeeping in the British Isles! However, the craft does provide enormous satisfaction and pleasure with prospects of a modest profit. Members of the community who are attracted to beekeeping nowadays are in many ways quite different from those who practised the craft in earlier times. For centuries beekeeping was a rural craft undertaken by cottagers and smallholders, or their wives, as a means of generating a little extra income. Today, because of profound changes in agricultural practices resulting in the loss of natural bee forage, many of the most profitable sites for honey production are no longer in the countryside but are surprisingly found in the suburbs of towns and cities. With mechanisation, the agricultural labour force has declined enormously and the old country crafts have become neglected. Those who are now attracted to the craft come from all walks of life, some through an interest in natural history and a fascination with honeybees whilst others enjoy the satisfaction of developing a skill in apiculture and the pleasure of producing a honey crop. Providing a docile strain of bee is kept and the hive sited in a sensible position it is possible to keep bees almost anywhere. Problems only arise when aggressive strains of bees are kept and are badly managed in close proximity to neighbours. Hopefully, the guidance and advice offered in the following pages will help the new beekeeper to understand the essentials of the craft so that it becomes an enduring source of pleasure, satisfaction, and modest profit. Perhaps for some, it will also be a refreshing diversion from the pressures of modern life.

CHAPTER 1

THE HONEYBEE

Honeybees are classified in the Genus Apis of the Hymenoptera Order of Insects. There are four well recognized distinct species of which, Apis mellifera is the most important for beekeepers. Originally, Apis mellifera was confined to Europe but in modern times it has been introduced into all continents so that today it is the most widely used hive-managed bee for honey production.

The other main species of honeybees are Apis dorsata, the Giant honeybee; Apis florea, the Little honeybee; and Apis cerana, the Asian hive bee. Recently, it has been suggested that Apis laboriosa, which resembles Apis dorsata, should be accepted as a fifth distinct species. All these honeybees, apart from Apis mellifera, are indigenous to Asia and only Apis mellifera and Apis cerana can be managed in hives.

Over the course of millions of years, by adaptation and evolution in separate geographical areas of the old world, Apis mellifera has developed a number of recognizable differences within the species so that today the following races, or varieties, can be described.

Italian (*Apis mellifera ligustica*)

To the apiculturist this is probably the most important variety of honeybee in the world today. Usually light in colour, the workers showing three yellow bands on the abdomen. They are normally good tempered, resistant to disease and reluctant to swarm. In the British Isles with unreliable summer weather conditions they have the disadvantage that they will rear brood excessively despite poor weather and make big demands on their food stores.

North European Dark Bees *(Apis mellifera mellifera)*

Included in this group are the Dutch, German, French and English dark brown and black bees. Generally, they form smaller colonies than the Italian types and winter well in northern climates. Some are aggressive and others are predisposed to frequent swarming. However, by selective breeding some good strains have been developed.

Carniolan *(Apis mellifera carnica)*

A very good tempered, slender, grey-haired bee, quiet on the combs and endowed with a long tongue. It originated in southern parts of Austria and Northern Greece. Withstands winter conditions well with rapid colony development in spring which may lead to swarming problems. One of the most important races in modern beekeeping.

Caucasian *(Apis mellifera causica)*

A docile, gentle bee which remains quiet on the combs. Reputed to have the longest tongue of all western honeybees. In appearance rather similar to the Carniolan. It has a low swarming tendency. Its main fault is that it uses propolis excessively and builds much brace comb, thus making comb manipulation in the hive rather tedious.

African and Africanized Bees

In the large continent of Africa, with its wide range of climatic and environmental conditions, the honeybee (Apis mellifera) has developed into a number of recognizable types but with a number of characteristics common to all of them. They tend to be aggressive and hard working, swarm readily, and abscond or migrate from their nests when nectar supplies diminish. They are much better adapted to sub-tropical conditions than the Italian or North European types of bee.

Because of their better adaptation to sub-tropical conditions a number of African queen bees were imported into Brazil in 1956 for controlled breeding and research purposes in an attempt to improve the indigenous bees. It was optimistically thought that the aggressive trait of the African bees could be eliminated by selective breeding. Perhaps not surprisingly, some of the cross-bred bees escaped. They proved to be very aggressive, their colony numbers multiplied quickly and when they inter-bred with European bees their African characteristics dominated. They soon spread through Brazil and most of South America continuing north through Central America reaching the borders of the U.S.A. There is no doubt that they are aggressive and incidents are well documented about their attacks on animals and humans. However, stories tend to become embellished with the telling and perhaps with proper management they are not as bad as they are painted. It appears that Brazilian beekeepers have had to change their methods but in doing so have found Africanized bees to be productive. Clearly, apiaries of these bees must be located away from populated districts and away from domestic animals.

CHAPTER 2

THE HONEYBEE COLONY

A prosperous colony of honeybees in summer consists of one queen, a few hundred drones and up to 80,000 workers. In addition there will be eggs, brood, honey and pollen in the combs. In the depth of winter the colony will be quite different: there will still be one queen, but the workers will be reduced to about 20,000 and the drones will have disappeared. There will probably be no eggs or brood but there should be sufficient stores of honey and pollen to last the colony until the spring. The colony can be said to wax to its maximum population in June or July and wane to its minimum in January or February.

The Queen

The queen is vital to a colony because she is its only fertile female and as such has the sole responsibility of producing all the eggs from which young bees are reared. At the height of the breeding season, in early summer, she produces enormous numbers of eggs. It has been estimated that a good queen of a prolific strain may lay more than 1,500 eggs each day for short periods when colony conditions are optimum.

Her other important function is to produce pheromones from her mandibular glands, called 'Queen substances', which the workers lick from her body and distribute amongst themselves. Pheromones are chemical substances the release of which into their surroundings by an animal influences the behaviour or development of other individuals of the same species. In this connection 'Queen substances' appear to be essential for the maintenance of the morale and cohesion of the colony

The queen and worker bees

and also for inhibiting egg laying by infertile workers. Virgin queens produce very little of these pheromones but mated laying queens produce them abundantly.

In general appearance the queen can be distinguished by her long abdomen, neatly folded wings, long legs and a relatively small head. The long legs, which are usually of a lighter colour than the body, give the queen a graceful movement over the combs and it is this which often attracts the beekeeper's eye when he is looking for her. The queen lives longer than other members of the colony, sometimes surviving several years, but her egg laying capacity diminishes after two full seasons. After she has mated she does not venture from the hive again, except with a swarm.

Workers

These are the smallest and most numerous bees in a colony. They are sexually undeveloped females and, as their name implies, they do all the work in the colony. It is of interest that the tasks they undertake follow a well recognized sequence from the time they are born.

Sequence of duties of workers from birth (emergence)

Age	Duties
1 to 3 days	Clean and polish comb cells
3 to 6 days	Feed older brood
6 to 10 days	Feed younger brood
8 to 12 days	Feed and groom Queen
11 to 18 days	House cleaners
12 to 18 days	Make wax and build combs
18 to 20 days	Guard duties
21 days onwards	Forage for pollen, nectar, water, propolis

In summer the life span of a worker is very short, perhaps no more than six weeks. It can be truly said that they work themselves to death since the labour involved in the production of a pound of honey is prodigious. It has been observed that bees largely forage within a radius of about two miles from their hives, although maximum efficiency in honey production is only achieved when nectar sources are no more than $1/4$ mile away. Each foraging trip may last an hour and in that time hundreds of flowers will be visited from which the bee might gather about 40 mgms of nectar. By the time this becomes honey the weight will be at least halved thereby indicating that something like 20,000 foraging trips are required to produce a pound of honey. Expressed another way, it has been calculated that to produce a pound of honey, bees may need to visit 15 million flowers!

Enormous quantities of pollen and nectar are collected and necessarily consumed by the bees for the essential day to day colony requirements of breeding, comb building, temperature maintenance etc., quite apart from that required for the basic sustenance of the individuals. A colony of only moderate size (40, 000 bees in summer) may collect and use 100 lb. of pollen and may also make 400 lb. of honey, of which it uses 300 to 350 lbs. The beekeeper's harvest represents the difference between the amounts collected and used, minus that which has to be left for winter provisions. The amount available to be taken from the hive at the end of the season is, therefore, open to wide variation.

Drones

The drone is a fertile male bee. He does no work for the colony, his only function being to mate with a young virgin queen should the opportunity arise. Mating, when it occurs, takes place on the wing usually at a height of 20 to 50 feet above ground level. The drone is larger than a worker, having a thick bulky abdomen, large wings and very large eyes. He does not have a sting. Drones usually begin to appear in a colony in late April and die rather miserably when the main nectar flows cease in August or September by being deprived of food and driven from the hive. During their short lives they tend to be on the wing in good weather, generally between about noon and 4 pm. Drones are very strong fliers and have a range of several miles. Although they normally return to their own colonies, they are allowed entry to hives other than their own in the summer season. When sexually mature they are known to be attracted to certain preferred locations in a vicinity where they congregate in the air. Interestingly, these favoured locations remain constant from year to year. Young virgin queens on their nuptial flights are attracted to these drone congregation areas.

Sexual Reproduction

A young virgin queen after emergence from her cell requires a few days in which to become sexually mature. When this is achieved she begins to take short flights from the hive, when the weather is good, to familiarize herself with the surroundings and position of her home; so-called orientation flights. Usually, when between five and ten days old she begins her mating flights. Mating takes place on the wing, normally some 20 to 50 feet above the ground and is effected by a number of drones. It is not uncommon for a queen to take two or three separate mating flights during which she may copulate with a total of a dozen drones. On return to the hive after mating she may still have attached to her parts of the genitalia torn from drones in the acts of copulation. Such fragments can sometimes be seen protruding from the end of her abdomen and are described by beekeepers as the 'mating sign'. The queen is soon cleaned by workers and a few days after her last flight she will begin to lay eggs. As is well known, drones die from their injuries sustained in mating. The sperm which the queen receives from drones is stored within her body in a sperm sac, or spermatheca. By a delicate mechanism, which is not completely understood, the liberation of sperm from the spermatheca is controlled. If sperm is liberated from the sperm sac when an egg passes nearby in the oviduct, then that egg will be fertilized. On the other hand, if the sperm sac remains closed, the egg will pass on its way to be laid in an unfertilized condition. Quite clearly there is a fundamental difference between fertilized and unfertilized eggs because the former will have a set of chromosomes from the father and mother, and are described as diploid, whilst the unfertilized eggs will have but a single set of chromosomes from the mother and are described as haploid. The practical importance of all this is that fertilized eggs can develop into queens or workers, whilst unfertilized eggs can only produce drones. Thus female bees (queens and workers) have a father and mother and can inherit characteristics from both parents, whereas the drone has no father and can therefore only inherit characteristics from the mother.

In the animal kingdom, successful sexual reproduction generally requires the fertilization of an ovum with a spermatozoa so that genetic material is merged from both parents. If this is not achieved the ovum dies. In the case of many ants, bees and wasps, however, unfertilized eggs develop into males. This remarkable phenomenon in which an egg develops without fertilization is called parthenogenesis.

Before laying an egg, the queen inspects the cell of the brood-comb to see that it has been properly cleaned by the house bees. If satisfied that it is suitable to receive an egg, she lowers her abdomen into it and deposits one on the floor of the cell. The egg is white in colour and is stuck to the floor in a perpendicular position. It measures about 1 mm in length and nearly $\frac{1}{3}$ mm in diameter. On the second day after being laid, the egg begins to lean over and by the third day it lies on its side on the bottom of the cell. At this stage, nurse bees surround the egg with 'bee milk' (brood food) in anticipation of the emergence of the tiny larva from the egg. Brood food is a highly nutritious milky fluid which is secreted by special glands (hypopharyngeal glands) which are situated in the head of the bee. The glands are most active in nurse bees between the age of 6 and 15 days. All larvae are fed on this 'bee milk' for the first two days, but after that only queen larvae are privileged to receive this special food in pure form, when it is often referred to as 'Royal Jelly'. From the third day the diet of worker and drone larvae is changed, the brood food being diluted with nectar and pollen and the amount given restricted to a quantity which is just sufficient for the adequate nourishment of the larvae. This is in marked contrast to the nourishment of queen larvae which are lavishly supplied with Royal Jelly, usually in excess of their needs.

Larvae grow very rapidly and to accommodate this increase in bulk they shed their external skin four times before they are sealed in their cells to pupate. The cells of queen and worker larvae are sealed on the 9th day whilst those of drone larvae are sealed on the 11th day. After being sealed in a cell the larva spins a cocoon and then undergoes a complete change from a grub to a pupa and finally to an adult bee. Queens will emerge from their cells about 16 days after the eggs were laid, workers 21 days, and drones 24 days. Workers and drones are reared in slightly different hexagonal cells of the combs in the brood nest. Worker larvae are accommodated in cells measuring about $\frac{1}{5}$ th inch across, whilst drone larvae are found in cells which are about 5% larger, there being only 4 to the linear inch. Furthermore, when the cells are sealed the drone cells have a domed capping which protrudes above the surface of the comb. Queen larvae are reared in special large acorn-shaped cells which are built out from the comb, most frequently along the sides or bottoms of the combs. These 'queen cells' hang vertically from the comb and measure about an inch and a quarter in length. They are quite distinctive and cannot really be confused with anything else.

Average Development Times of Brood (Days)

	Queen	Worker	Drone
Incubation of egg	3	3	3
Unsealed larva	5	5	7
Sealed pupa	7	13	14
Total time to emergence	16	21	24

CHAPTER 3

HIVES AND BASIC EQUIPMENT

When early civilizations progressed from honey hunting to beekeeping there was a requirement for receptacles in which to accommodate bees. Originally, these were hollow containers of some sort into which swarms were introduced and allowed to build natural combs. For centuries, in Europe, these containers were skeps made of straw or wickerwork, whilst in other areas hollow logs were exploited and in some Mediterranean countries earthenware pots were used. The combs were firmly anchored inside all these containers so that the only way to obtain honey was to either kill the bees at the end of the season, or to drive them out. Many attempts were made to develop hives in which the combs were attached to wooden bars or frames, with the objective of making them removable for inspection and extraction of honey. Invariably, however, the bees fixed everything firmly to the insides of the hives. In 1851, Rev. Langstroth in America, made the fundamentally important observation that bees would not fill a space above and around combs if it measured about $\frac{1}{4}$ inch. This critical measurement has become known as the 'bee-space'. All modern hives are constructed to incorporate this space around the combs and as a result the combs are readily movable.

Essentially, a modern hive consists of a floor with a bee entrance, on which rests a box, open at the top and bottom, known as the brood chamber. This is covered by an inner lid, called the crown board, above which is a weatherproof roof. The brood chamber is constructed so that wooden frames holding the combs will hang in them with the correct bee-space all around. By their construction, or by the use of special spacers, the frames are held with an appropriate space between them.

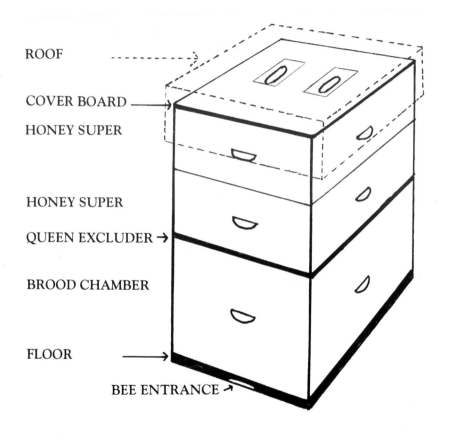

ROOF

COVER BOARD

HONEY SUPER

HONEY SUPER

QUEEN EXCLUDER →

BROOD CHAMBER

FLOOR

BEE ENTRANCE ↗

Configuration of a single-walled hive in summer

As the name implies, the brood chamber is the part of the hive in which brood is reared and is, therefore, the area in which the queen resides. In winter a hive will consist of a floor, brood box and contained combs, crown board and roof. In summer, to provide space for the storage of honey, the hive is enlarged by adding further boxes, called 'supers', above the brood chamber and below the crown board.

Choice of Hive

There are six designs of hives available in this country at the present time, namely, the W.B.C., Modified National, Smith, Modified Commercial, Langstroth and Modified Dadant. They are all normally made of wood, preferably cedar, but synthetic materials are being tried. Until these are proven it would be wise to stick to the conventional material. The W.B.C. is a double-walled hive, whilst all the others are single-walled. Unfortunately, there is no agreed 'best hive' and it is, therefore, difficult to make a dogmatic recommendation. On the other hand, it seems illogical to expect someone with no knowledge of the craft to make a choice. Before making any purchases it would, therefore, be wise for the beginner to discuss the matter with established local beekeepers, to seek guidance on the type of hive favoured in their particular area. For those wishing to delve more deeply into the pros and cons of the various hive types the book 'A Case of Hives' by Len Heath is highly recommended. Whatever the final choice it should be remembered that it is most desirable to have only one design of hive in an apiary, so that hive parts, frames etc., can be interchanged if necessary. There is no good evidence that a double-walled hive has any advantage over a single-walled hive as far as the bees are concerned. Indeed, I think it fair to say that bees can be kept successfully in any type of hive providing they have sufficient space and their accommodation gives them protection from the weather. Some people consider that the W.B.C. looks more attractive than the other types when bees are kept in the garden, but against that must be balanced the increased cost. The W.B.C. is really only suitable as a static hive, it is definitely a disadvan-

The old and new. Left a straw skep hive; right a Modified Dadant Hive

tage if migratory beekeeping is contemplated. My advice therefore to the beginner is to avoid the W.B.C., unless the intended beekeeping activities will be limited to a couple of hives in the garden.

Throughout the world the Langstroth is the most commonly used hive but in the U.K. the Modified National is the one most favoured. On balance, therefore, the beginner here will not go far wrong in choosing the latter providing it is realized that it is not perfect in the eyes of everyone! The main criticism of it is that the brood chamber is not large enough to accommodate the modern strains of prolific bees. It should be remembered that the small size of the British standard brood frame (14 inches long and 8½ inches deep), as used in the Modified National hive, was decided upon in 1882 by the British Beekeepers Association at the time when the craft was changing from skep beekeeping to the

26

National hive (two brood chambers and two supers). Note the unwanted gap between the brood chambers which will allow robbers to enter and the repaired woodpecker damage to supers

WBC Hive (right); four comb nucleus hive (left)

use of movable frame hives. The bees at that time were the English Black variety, a non-prolific type suited to skeps. That bee no longer exists having been wiped out by acarine disease some seventy years ago. Following that disaster the U.K. was re-stocked with bees imported from the Continent, many of which were more prolific in character. With those facts in mind it is perhaps surprising that so many beekeepers in this country today, whilst keeping relatively prolific bees, still adhere to hive and frame sizes decided quite arbitrarily by a committee more than a century ago for a particular bee which is now extinct! It is interesting to note that the chosen small size of the British standard frame was actually being criticized by some progressive beekeepers before the demise of the Black bee. In his 1914 book, 'The Modern Bee Farm', Simmins wrote *"I must state without hesitation that the standard frame of the British Beekeepers Association is too small for any beekeeper who is attempting to produce honey on a wholesale scale"*. Later, in the 1930's R.O.B. Manley, a well known bee farmer, extolled the virtues of large hives and frames and coming right up to the present time Brother Adam of Buckfast Abbey uses Modified Dadant hives. Today, it is widely accepted that the National hive requires more room for brood rearing. Many beekeepers, therefore, enlarge the brood chamber by the addition of a second brood box, or by adding a super to the brood box for the queen to use. These measures will give adequate space but there is the disadvantage that there will be 22 combs to manipulate during routine inspections. Some beekeepers, including the author, prefer hives with larger brood boxes containing larger frames so that the brood nest is contained in a single box. The Modified Commercial and Modified Dadant hives meet this requirement but it has to be said that the extra weight make them more difficult to move if migratory beekeeping is undertaken.

DIMENSIONS OF FRAMES

Frame Type (in)	Top Bar Length (in)	Comb Length (in)	Comb Depth (in)	Comb Area (sq. in)
B.S. Brood	17	14	8 1/2	119
B.S. Shallow	17	14	5 1/2	77
Mod. Com. Brood	17 1/4	16	10	160
Mod. Com. Shallow	17 1/4	16	6	96
Langstroth Brood	19	17 5/8	9 1/8	161
Langstroth Shallow	19	17 5/8	5 3/8	95
M.D. Brood	19	17 5/8	11 1/4	198
M.D. Shallow	19	17 5/8	6 1/4	110

BROOD BOX COMB CAPACITIES

Hive	Frame Type	No. of Combs	Total Comb Area (sq. in)	Equivalent No. of B.S. Frames
W.B.C.	B.S.	10	1988	10
National	B.S.	11	2186	11
Smith	B.S. (15 1/2 in top bars)	11	2186	11
M. Comm	16 in x 10 in	11	3020	15.1
Langstroth	Lang.	10	2742	13.8
M.D.	M.D.	11	3805	19.1

Looking into the top of a hive showing spacing of frames

Frames

The various frame sizes have been given in the table. Frames are conventionally made of wood but plastic types can also be obtained. When in use in the brood chamber, or honey supers, they should be spaced evenly apart, about 1³/₈ in. from comb centre to centre. There are a number of methods of doing this but for British Standard frames, metal or plastic spacers which slip over the ends of the frame top bars are commonly used. These are, however, rather fiddly and are best avoided. Self-spacing frames of the Hoffman type are to be preferred. In these the spacing device is an integral part of the frame side bar, the upper two inches of which is expanded as a shoulder to hold the combs the correct distance apart.

Frames used in honey supers are generally just shallow versions of the brood combs used in a particular hive type. However, there is one pattern of frame designed for use in supers only, known as the Manley frame, which has advantages. In this type the side bars are wide and make contact with adjacent frames down their whole length, thus holding the frames rigidly. The spacing of the frames is a little wider than usual being $1\,^3/_4$ inches so fewer frames can be accommodated in a standard super box but as the combs are a little thicker the honey content of a super is not diminished. Bees usually build nice even combs in these frames which are easy to uncap because the top and bottom bars are of identical width.

Wax Foundation

Sheets of pure beeswax foundation, on which is impressed the hexagonal cell pattern of natural honeycomb, are fitted into the frames before they are placed in the hive. All foundation for use in the brood chamber should be of 'worker' type, which means it should have five hexagonal cells to the linear inch, and the sheets should be reinforced with tinned wires running through them. Similar foundation should be used in the super frames if it is intended to work for extracted honey. If, however, comb honey is required then it is best to use special thin unwired foundation. Some beekeepers like to use 'drone base' foundation (i.e. 4 cells to the linear inch) in the supers but this is not recommended for the beginner. Providing bees with wax foundation enables them to build combs evenly and quickly and saves them much energy. It has been estimated that bees may use 5 to 6 lbs of honey in the making of one pound of wax.

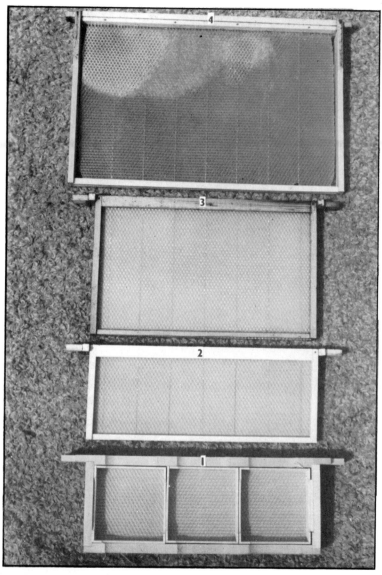

Frames containing foundation
1. Hanging section frame
2. Standard shallow super frame
3. Standard brood frame
4. Modified Dadant brood frame

Queen Excluder

It is desirable to confine brood rearing to the brood chamber, leaving the supers for the storage of honey. To ensure this the movement of the queen must be restricted so that she cannot get into the supers. To achieve this a barrier has to be interposed between the brood chamber and the honey supers which will confine the queen to her proper area but will not obstruct the free passage of workers into the supers to store honey. This barrier is called a queen excluder. The simplest type is a sheet of zinc in which slots are punched of such exact size that worker bees can pass through, but not the larger queen or drones. Another type, which is a little more expensive, is made of stiff parallel wires, suitably spaced and framed. Queen excluders are placed on the top of the brood chamber and below the honey supers

Other Necessary Equipment

A bee-veil is essential to protect the head, face, eyes and neck from stings. It should always be worn when opening a hive. To manipulate bees without a veil is neither brave nor clever; it is foolish! A beginner will be well advised to wear a bee-proof overall and gloves until some confidence and tolerance of stings is achieved.

An efficient smoker is required to subdue and control bees when a hive is open. It is very worthwhile to buy a good one of adequate size, because the small types have an irritating habit of going out just when they are urgently needed. The large bent-nosed variety is the best.

Another basic item of equipment which greatly facilitates hive manipulations is a proper hive-tool. This is a multi-purpose steel instrument designed to expedite various tasks, such as separating hive parts, moving frames, scraping off wax and propolis etc.

Bees, when they are first installed in a hive will require feeding, and also at other times such as in bad summers when there is a dearth of normal food supplies. Proprietary appliances for feeding sugar syrup can be purchased but it is not too difficult to make a simple feeder from a large treacle tin which has a press-in lid that makes a good seal. All that is required is to punch a few holes in the lid with a fine nail. When the tin is filled with sugar syrup, and the lid applied, it can be inverted over the feed hole in the crown board. The bees will suck the syrup from the tin through the small holes.

CHAPTER 4

HOW TO START

T he first requirement is to obtain a hive and the basic
equipment, preferably before the start of the active beekeeping season. If the hive is second-hand it should be cleaned
very carefully to make sure it does not carry disease. The floor-board,
brood box, supers, cover board etc. should be scraped free of all wax and
propolis and then sterilized by flaming with a blow-lamp. The heat
applied should be sufficient to remove all excreta and other organic
matter without burning the wood. The outsides of the lifts of W.B.C.
hives can be painted but it is not desirable to paint single wall hives. The
outsides of the latter are best treated with a non-toxic wood preserva-
tive, or an exterior microporous wood stain, which allows the wood to
'breathe'. The insides of brood boxes, supers, floors and roofs should
never be painted or treated with preservatives.

If a second-hand hive was purchased and found to contain old frames
or combs these should, without hesitation, be disposed of on a bonfire
as they may carry disease.

Apiary Site

Careful thought should always be given to the positioning of an apiary.
Firm ground with good drainage is required: a site which becomes
water-logged in winter is unsuitable for bees. It is ideal if hives can face
east, south or west and have a hedge or other wind-break behind them
to give protection against northerly winds. In a garden site it is also
useful to have some shrubs, or trellis work on which climbers can be
trained, a few feet in front of the hives to make the bees fly above head
height. The hives should be placed 4 to 6 feet apart and if their

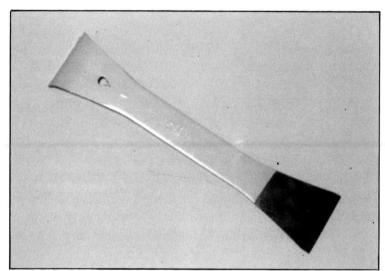

Hive tool

Equipment
1. McCord frame grip
2. Bee brush
3. Gauntlet bee gloves
4. Smoker
5. Bee veil and hat

entrances can face in different directions so much the better as this will help the bees in their orientation and diminish drifting from one colony to another. Sufficient room should be allowed for the beekeeper to work hives from the rear.

Hives should never be placed directly on bare ground: they should be set on firm stands to raise them clear of the ground and they should stand level. Long grass and weeds around hives should be kept trimmed so as not to obstruct the flight path of the bees.

Feeders
1. *A popular rapid feeder*
2. *Plastic paint kettle made into a contact feeder by perforating the lid*
3. *A large capacity Miller rapid feeder*
4. *A honey tin made into a contact feeder by perforating the lid*

Essential Equipment

A bee-veil, hive tool, smoker and feeder should be obtained. As indicated in the previous chapter, a simple feeder can be home-made. A large smoker is the most efficient, fuel for which can be corrugated cardboard, old sacking, or dried rotten wood. If old sacking is used care should be taken to ensure that it has not been contaminated with insecticides or other toxic chemicals. Rotting birch wood is usually plentiful in any mixed woodland and is very satisfactory smoker fuel when dried.

The Bees

It is essential that the beginner starts with bees that are healthy and of manageable docile temperament. Probably the best way of achieving this is to buy a four or six comb nucleus, headed by a young queen, from a local reputable beekeeper or from one of the well known commercial producers. Some Beekeepers Associations produce nuclei for sale to their members at very reasonable prices. The alternative way of starting is with a swarm. This has the advantage of low initial cost but it has some important disadvantages which will be discussed later in this chapter.

Sometimes, it is possible to buy a complete colony from a beekeeper who is over-stocked, or is giving up the craft. Providing the bees are healthy and docile it is often possible to pick up a bargain this way but it must be said that some beginners who are completely lacking in practical experience might be intimidated by having to deal with a full size colony from the outset. It's jumping in at the deep end!

Starting with a Nucleus

A nucleus is a small colony of bees with a queen together with a limited number of combs containing brood and food. A four comb nucleus, headed by a young queen, and purchased from a reputable supplier who will guarantee that the bees are healthy and docile, is undoubtedly the best way to start beekeeping. The nucleus should be obtained as early as possible in the season, preferably in May. By starting with a small number of bees the novice will gain confidence and experience in step with the development of the colony. There may not be any surplus honey in the first season but in good years there might be a little. The profit of the first season is experience.

A nucleus is usually delivered in a purpose-made travelling box which accommodates securely the number of combs supplied. The box should have large ventilation panels of wire gauze and a flight entrance which is closed during transit. As soon as the bees arrive, place the box as close as possible next to the hive in which they are to be accommodated, with the flight entrance of the travelling box facing the same direction as that of the hive. Having done that, carefully remove the cover from the flight entrance of the box and let the bees fly for an hour or so. During this time they will settle down and orientate to the position of their new home.

To transfer the nucleus into the new hive blow a little smoke into the entrance of the travelling box and through the ventilating screen. After a couple of minutes, carefully, without jolting, remove the lid of the box and then transfer the combs to the hive, one by one, with a deliberate smooth action, taking care not to dislodge the bees covering the combs. The combs should be placed in the hive in the same order and relative position to each other as they were in the travelling box. Whilst being transferred the combs should be quickly checked to see that there is brood in all stages of development and a balanced proportion of brood to food. The requirement of the British Standard Specification B.S.S. 1372 : 1947 is, briefly, that there should be no visible signs of disease,

A plastic one-gallon feeder

that there should be a laying queen, worker brood in all stages covering at least half the comb area, an average of 1 1/4 lb. of honey and pollen per comb and sufficient bees to cover all the combs.

The queen will probably be seen during the transfer, but it is not desirable to spend a lot of time searching for her if all appears well. If the travelling box was left for an hour or so with the bees flying before transfer it is most probable that the queen will have positioned herself on a comb in the centre of the box. If, however, after transferring the combs she is seen on the side or bottom of the box, she must be gently coaxed on to the combs in the hive before shaking out the remaining bees. Normally, the queen will be seen on a comb during the transfer and in those circumstances when all the combs are in the hive all that is required is to shake any bees remaining in the travelling box into the hive.

When all the bees and combs are in the hive a frame of foundation is added on each side of the nucleus to allow for colony expansion. All the frames are closed up to one side of the brood box and a dummy board is placed next to the uncovered frame of foundation which is towards the centre of the hive. A dummy board is simply a flat piece of wood cut to the same size and shape as a brood frame. It functions as a movable inner wall to the brood nest so that the available volume of the brood box can be easily adjusted. It has long been observed that a small colony does not prosper quickly when placed in an unrestricted full size brood box. It is much better to enlarge the brood area gradually by adding frames of foundation and moving the dummy board as the needs of the colony increase.

Finally, the cover board and roof are applied and the hive entrance reduced to a width of about two inches.

A nucleus, after installation in a new hive, should be fed with warm sugar syrup made by dissolving white granulated sugar in water in the proportion of 2 lb. of sugar in one pint of water. This is best given in a slow feeder and should be continued whilst foundation is being drawn into comb and the brood nest is developing. Frames of foundation are added to the nucleus, perhaps a couple every few days, as required until the brood chamber is full. When adding frames of foundation always place them on the outside of the existing combs and never insert them in the centre so that they divide the brood nest.

When the brood chamber is full of drawn combs covered with bees, a super can be added above a queen excluder but, as stated earlier, quantities of surplus honey must not be expected. In this first season the real purpose of the nucleus is to build itself into a strong viable colony from which benefits will come in future years.

Starting with a Swarm

This is undoubtedly the cheapest way to start because a swarm can usually be collected for nothing. If you join your local Beekeepers Association and let the Secretary know that you wish to start beekeeping and would like a swarm, you will find that everyone will do their best to help you.

Having obtained a swarm, this can be hived in the way described in **Chapter 6**. Feeding will be required because the only food immediately available to the bees is that which they carried with them in their honey stomachs. The initial feed should be 7 lbs of sugar as syrup, dissolving 2 lbs of sugar in one pint of water. After this first feed a weaker syrup can be used made in the proportions of 1 lb. of sugar to one pint of water. This should be continued until the brood nest is complete, at which stage a honey super can be placed on the hive, above a queen excluder.

If a swarm is small and will clearly not use all the frames in the brood box then, after a few days, the frames should be reduced to the number covered by the bees. The occupied frames should be drawn to one side of the brood box and closed on the other side with a dummy board as described earlier in the management of a nucleus. Additional frames can be added later as the brood nest expands, but it should be remembered that a swarm always decreases in population during the first three weeks of its existence and after that begins to build up. This is because there are no young bees emerging in the first three weeks to replace the old bees as they die.

The risk that a good strong swarm carries disease is not high but, nevertheless, it is wise to be cautious. As soon as possible after a swarm is hived, a sample of bees should be sent for examination for adult bee diseases. A service for the diagnosis of disease in adult bees is usually available in those counties which still employ a County Beekeeping Instructor. Sadly, there are now very few enlightened counties with such staff. Details of any local facilities can be obtained from the secretary of your Beekeepers Association. If no local service is available samples can be sent to the National Beekeeping Specialist, Luddington Experimental Horticultural Station, Stratford-upon-Avon, CV37 9SJ but a charge will be made. At the time of writing this is £7.50 plus VAT per sample. Details of this and other services can be obtained on application to the National Beekeeping Unit, Luddington.

A sample for examination should consist of not less than 30 live bees, all taken from the same hive, placed in a match box or similar container (not a tin or plastic box or bag), clearly labelled with the name and address of the sender and the number or identification mark of the hive concerned. Relevant information about the sample and the colony from which it was taken should be given in an accompanying note enclosed in the package. A match-box containing a sample of bees, with accompanying letter, will travel quite safely in a thick envelope by first class letter post.

Old bees are best for laboratory examination: very young bees from the face of a brood comb should not be sent. A quick and simple method of securing a sample is to scoop the bees into an inverted match-box tray, keeping them trapped under the tray whilst the cover is slid on. This method can be used most conveniently on a flat surface which is covered with bees, such as the underside of a crown board or along the top bars of the brood frames. To see how many bees have been captured, without releasing them, place the match-box under a small piece of glass and the tray can then be slid out to reveal the contents.

The report on the health of the adult bees sent in the sample is usually available in a few days. If this is satisfactory, the next important precaution is to check for brood diseases. This should be done regularly from about the third week onwards when brood in all stages will be present. The important brood diseases are described in **Chapter 13** and the beginner should familiarize himself with the main features of these diseases. Unfortunately, disease in the early stages is not easily spotted by the untutored eye, so if possible the novice should ask an experienced beekeeper to help. If disease is seriously suspected, the Bee Disease Officer of the Ministry of Agriculture should be contacted through the Secretary of the local Beekeepers Association.

When it has been confirmed that the swarm is healthy, it is highly desirable that it should be re-queened with a young queen from a healthy docile strain. This is because the age of the swarm queen will be unknown, but the probability is that she is not less than two years old and getting past her best. Furthermore, important undesirable characteristics such as aggressiveness, excessive swarming tendency and low vigour may be present in the progeny of the swarm queen. For all these reasons it is best to re-queen with a young queen from a reliable strain. The method of re-queening is described in **Chapter 7**.

CHAPTER 5

MANAGEMENT THROUGH THE YEAR

I n the annual cycle of activities of a colony of bees, early autumn marks the end of one cycle and the beginning of the next. At that time all the great labours of spring and summer are over, the harvest of nectar stored as honey, and the beekeeper will have taken what is surplus to the needs of the bees. After the culmination of all those activities the colony will be entering a period of apparent dormancy and it is appropriate that the beekeeper should then reflect on the successes and failures of the season past and make plans and good resolutions for the future. In that sense the new beekeeping year begins in the autumn.

Autumn Management

The ability of a colony of honeybees to produce a good harvest of honey during the summer season is dependent upon its survival in good condition through the winter, and upon its growth in strength and vigour in the spring. In order to do this, a colony must have a fertile queen, it should be healthy, it should have adequate stocks of suitable food, and it should be housed in a hive which is water-proof and gives good protection against inclement weather. The steps necessary to ensure that these basic requirements are satisfied should be planned soon after the main honey crop has been removed in August.

The four main items requiring attention, therefore, are the re-queening of colonies having old or unsatisfactory queens, feeding, making hive entrances mouseproof, and repairing and securing hives to withstand the hazards of winter.

Re-queening

A fertile young queen has the best chance of surviving a long cold winter and apart from this has other advantages. Young queens will usually continue laying eggs into late autumn. This benefits the colony because young bees are those most likely to survive the winter and will also be in the best condition to face the hazards of early spring foraging for pollen and water. Furthermore, a young queen will usually start egg laying early in the year which is essential if the colony is to build up to sufficient strength to exploit early sources of nectar as provided by oilseed rape. Swarming is also less likely in colonies headed by a young vigorous queen. For all these reasons it is good beekeeping practice to discard queens after they have completed two full seasons and replace with young mated queens of a reliable strain. Queens heading colonies that have proved bad-tempered or otherwise unsatisfactory should also be replaced. Late August or early September is probably the easiest time to re-queen. Details of a simple method are given in **Chapter 7**.

Feeding

When the honey crop is removed from a hive the beekeeper must accept responsibility for the well-being of the colony by ensuring that the bees have adequate food reserves to tide them over periods of inclement weather. Some bees will store all their reserves above the brood nest in the supers and when these are removed starvation is possible if adverse weather ensues. A rough idea of food reserves in the brood chamber can be obtained by 'hefting' the hive. In this technique the hive is tilted forwards by lifting it with a hand placed under the floor at the rear. A well provisioned colony will feel heavy whereas one short of food will feel very light. With practice the differences in hive weights become obvious.

If a colony feels light when the honey supers are removed it should be fed with not less than a gallon of thick sugar syrup, made by dissolving 2 lbs of sugar in each pint of water. This food is for the immediate sustenance of the colony and has no relevance to the provision of winter stores. The need for feeding to provide winter stores should be assessed in late August or early September.

A good strong colony of honeybees needs at least 50 lbs of suitable stores to see it through the winter and to provide adequate reserves to enable breeding to go ahead unhindered in the early months of the year. In extra large colonies, such as found in Dadant hives, more than 60 lbs of winter stores may be required.

Towards the end of August the food reserves of a colony should be assessed and if the estimate is below the minimum requirement feeding should be undertaken. This should be thick sugar syrup, made by dissolving 2 lbs of white granulated sugar in each pint of water, and given in such amount as to bring the food reserves in the hive above the minimum requirement. When feeding for winter stores the sugar syrup should be given rapidly. This can be achieved very conveniently in feeders of the 'Miller' or 'Ashforth' types. All feeding should be completed by the end of September at the latest.

Preparation of the Hive

Hives should be inspected to make sure that they are in good repair and water-proof. Bees can withstand any cold weather we are likely to experience in this country, providing they are dry. They will quickly succumb in a cold, wet hive. Ventilation of the brood chamber is necessary throughout the winter to disperse the water vapour produced by the respiration of the bees. Food is consumed to release energy to provide essential warmth in the cluster which is vital for survival. When honey, or sugar, which are simple carbohydrates, are consumed and metabolized by the bee to release energy, the waste products are carbon dioxide and water vapour. These are eliminated by the bee, as in humans, by the process of respiration. For good wintering, adequate ventilation without draughts, is, therefore, needed.

The hive entrance should be left open about nine inches, protected by a mouseguard. If mice get into a hive they can cause great damage to the combs. The opportunity for them to gain entry is in winter when the bees are clustered and not active enough to repel intruders. Commercially available mouseguards are usually strips of perforated metal with holes $^3/_8$ inch in diameter through which bees can pass, but small enough to exclude mice. These should be firmly fixed across the hive entrance. Alternatively, a piece of perforated zinc gauze can be used by cutting an aperture along the bottom edge 9 inches long and $^3/_8$ inch high and fixing this securely across the entrance.

The brood chamber should be covered with a crown board and the feed hole covered with a piece of perforated zinc. Some beekeepers prefer to leave the feed hole uncovered to ensure good through ventilation. Above the crown board can be placed a piece of $^1/_2$ inch insulation board, cut to the same size as the crown board, with holes cut in it to coincide with the feed holes so as not to obstruct ventilation. An alternative to insulation board is a double layer of clean hessian sacking. No other packing above the crown board should be necessary. Ventilation in winter is considered to be so important by some beekeepers that they raise the crown board off the brood chamber by placing matchsticks under the corners, thereby increasing the air flow considerably. Others discard the crown board completely and simply cover the brood frames with a canvas or hessian quilt. It should be noted that if the crown board is raised for winter ventilation it should be lowered early in the new year, otherwise the bees will have difficulty in maintaining adequate heat in the brood chamber for the young brood. Depending on the weather, a good queen will start to lay small numbers of eggs soon after Xmas.

In woodland sites woodpeckers can be a problem, their strong beaks can quickly drill a hole through a softwood hive leaving the clustering bees exposed for the birds to plunder. The simplest way to protect a hive against these predators is to cover it with 1 inch mesh wire netting. To deter the birds some beekeepers cover their hives with used polythene fertilizer or waste bags. However, from many years experience, wire netting has been found to be entirely effective. It has the added advantage that it allows air to circulate freely around the hive allowing the wood to 'breathe' and disperse any moisture which works its way through from the inside.

The final precaution in exposed sites is to tie down the roof so that it will not be blown off by winter gales. Sometimes it is necessary to anchor the whole hive by roping it to stakes in the ground.

Winter Management

Bees winter best when the weather is generally cold but broken by brief mild spells. In the mild interludes the bees can take cleansing flights and in the brood chamber the cluster can expand and if necessary move over to fresh stores. From November to February colonies should not be disturbed. However, occasional visits to the apiary are desirable to make sure that hives are intact and to check that entrances have not become blocked by dead bees.

In a very mild winter, bees will remain active and continue to raise brood. In these circumstances the beekeeper must be alert to the possibility that winter stores may be exhausted more quickly than expected. A rough idea of the speed at which stores are being used can be obtained by 'hefting' the hives at routine apiary visits during the winter and spring. If by this procedure it becomes apparent that a hive is becoming very light in weight then food must be given. Sugar syrup is unsuitable food in winter but an acceptable alternative is soft sugar candy. This can be purchased or made at home. It is cheaper to make at home and it does seem that the freshly made product is more attractive to the bees.

Recipe for Soft Candy

Into a large saucepan or preserving pan place one pint of water and bring to the boil. Gradually stir in 6 lbs of white granulated sugar. Apply gentle heat and stir until the sugar is dissolved. Add a half-teaspoon of cream of tartar and apply brisk heat, stirring all the time. Bring to the boil and when the temperature reaches 235 °F on a sugar thermometer, remove the pan from the heat and place in the sink surrounded by cold water. When the sugar solution has cooled to between 120 °F and 140 °F stir vigorously and as soon as the mixture begins to stiffen pour quickly into moulds. Half-gallon plastic icecream containers are very convenient moulds.

The above method requires the use of a sugar boiling thermometer and undoubtedly this is the easiest way. However, when working without a thermometer, bring the mixture to the boil, reduce the heat and allow to boil for about half a minute. Test by dropping a small quantity of the mixture on a cold plate and when cool enough, press with the finger. If the sugar does not stick to the finger, it has boiled enough. If, however, it remains sticky, it must be boiled a little longer.

The finished product should be firm but not rock hard. Neither should it be so soft that when put on the hive it becomes semi-solid and starts to liquefy.

To feed the bees, place the container of candy face downwards over the open feed hole in the crown board and cover it with a piece of sacking to help keep it warm. Examine at regular intervals and give more as necessary.

Spring Management

During March, the brood nest will be expanding and there will be increasing demands for fresh pollen and water. Whenever the weather allows, the bees will forage actively and although pollen and water may be available it is unlikely that there will be a sufficiency of nectar to meet the daily food requirement. Food stores will, therefore, begin to diminish rapidly as brood rearing increases. March is probably the most dangerous month for losing colonies from starvation so a careful check must be kept on the weight of hives. Any colony that appears to be underweight should be fed with strong sugar syrup (2 lbs of white sugar to one pint of water). At least a gallon of this syrup should be given in a rapid feeder, preferably a contact type placed immediately above the brood nest because in cold weather bees may be reluctant to move up into a Miller type feeder.

Much useful information can be gathered by observing the hive entrance in spring. On mild days, when the temperature is more than 10 °C, the bees should be very active around mid-day. If they are seen to be taking large quantities of pollen into the hive, the beekeeper can have some confidence that the colony has a queen and is rearing brood. During the mild spells the bees will do their best to clean the hive and in this process numbers of dead bees will be removed and deposited outside the front of the hive. This is normal. If, however, the number seems excessive and especially if there are many weak crawling bees, further investigation is required. The cause may be starvation so the hive should be hefted to test its weight. If it is underweight the bees should be fed immediately with a gallon of warm thick sugar syrup. If starvation is extreme the best emergency measure is to remove an empty comb from the brood nest and gently pour thick warm sugar syrup into the empty cells of this comb and when it is as full as possible replacing it in the brood nest. By doing this the food is placed as near as possible to the weak starving bees. This will resuscitate them and give them sufficient strength to take the remainder of the feed from a rapid feeder of the contact type. If starvation is eliminated as the cause of the dead and crawling bees then disease must be suspected. A sample should be collected, as described in **Chapter 4**, and sent for examination for adult bee diseases.

On a warm sunny day in early April, a quick first examination of a colony can be made. The purpose of this examination is to ascertain that food stores are adequate and that healthy worker brood is present. This should be done with as little disturbance of the brood nest as possible. If healthy worker brood is seen it can be concluded that a laying queen is present and time should not be wasted searching for her. Prolonged disturbance of a hive in the early part of the year must be avoided as there is a danger that brood will be chilled. There is also a small risk at this time of year that the bees will form a tight cluster around the queen, 'balling' her and suffocating her to death. The loss of a queen in early spring is a catastrophe for that colony, because even if they rear another queen, it is very unlikely that there will be mature drones flying with whom she can mate. The colony will be left with an infertile queen and as such has no future. If it is not possible to obtain a fertile queen for it then the best that can be done is to unite it with another queen-right colony.

Patchy, scattered sealed brood, in worker cells with markedly domed cappings will indicate one of two things, either the queen is a 'drone layer', meaning that she is only laying unfertilized eggs. or that there are laying workers in the hive following the loss of the queen. These also lay unfertilized eggs. If there is a drone laying queen in a colony she should be culled and the stock united with a queen-right colony as soon as possible. A colony with laying workers can be more difficult and should only be united with a very strong queen-right stock. A small colony with laying workers is not really worth bothering with. The method of uniting colonies is given in **Chapter 7**.

When the bees become active in the spring mouseguards at the hive entrances are no longer required. They should then be removed. To retain warmth in the brood chamber, hive entrances should be limited in width to about five inches.

It is impossible to be dogmatic about the precise dates when colonies should be examined in spring because seasonal weather patterns are the important factors and not the calendar. In recent years there have been a number of very mild winters causing spring to be nearly a month early. In those circumstances bee colonies also develop early and apiary work should, therefore, be brought forward. The dates mentioned in this chapter are those relevant to what might be described as an 'average weather year'.

Colonies which are found to be satisfactory, with healthy worker brood and adequate food reserves at the first examination, will not, generally speaking, require further attention until late April, or early May, when a second and more thorough inspection should be made. The exception to this is where colonies are being prepared to exploit the oil seed rape crop which flowers early in the year. Such colonies benefit from extra attention as will be described in **Chapter 8**.

The second examination should be done on a warm sunny day so that the beekeeper is not hurried. The purpose of this examination will be to remove unserviceable combs from the brood chamber, to clean the floor board, to scrape burr comb and propolis from the tops of the frames, and to inspect for disease. It should also be confirmed that the queen is present and is laying well. The development of the colony should be assessed and if brood is present on four or five combs and bees are occupying the outer frames then a honey super containing drawn combs should be put on the hive, above a queen excluder. The beekeeper should always try to anticipate the need of the bees for extra space and to provide it as soon as it is required because overcrowding of the brood chamber is one factor which encourages swarming.

If the combs in the brood box are only one or two years old, it is only necessary to remove any outer, unoccupied combs which are misshapen or otherwise in poor condition, together with combs which do not completely fill the frames or contain excessive quantities of drone cells. Frames of comb should preferably be used to replace those removed but if these are not available then frames of foundation can be used. New frames of comb or foundation should be placed on the flanks of the brood nest and never put into the centre.

After a long winter confinement, the floor board may be covered with debris consisting of dead bees, cappings, old wax and propolis. The brood chamber should be lifted to one side and the floor board scraped clean. It can then be sterilized by flaming with a blow lamp.

If all the combs in a brood chamber are old, and especially if the colony has suffered with the disease Nosema, it is highly desirable to discard all the combs and get the colony on to a new set. This can be done in early May as follows. Make up a brood box containing either clean drawn combs or foundation, leaving one frame space empty in the centre of the box. Next, find the queen in the old brood box and remove her on the comb on which she is present and place this in the vacant centre space in the new brood box. Mark this old frame with a drawing pin in the upper surface of the top bar. Close up the frames in the old brood box, place upon it a queen excluder and then add the new brood box containing the queen. If the hive has already been supered then a further queen excluder should be placed above the new brood box before adding the supers. To encourage the queen to lay in her new brood box and help the workers build comb it is desirable to feed a pint of sugar syrup daily in a slow feeder for at least a week.

After one week examine the new brood box. If the weather has been reasonably warm, the queen should have moved off the old comb and should be seen laying eggs on a new one. The old marked comb can then be removed and placed back in the original brood box below the queen excluder. The combs in the new brood box should be moved together to fill the space left by the removal of the old comb and a frame of foundation, or drawn comb, put in an outside position to complete a full set. The hive is then reassembled with the queen excluders in exactly the same positions as previously described. After three weeks, all the brood in the bottom box will have emerged and this box containing the old combs can then be removed.

Some strains of bees are very prolific, notably those of Italian type, and if WBC or Modified National hives are used it is most probable that the bees will require a double brood chamber arrangement. In such hives it is convenient to change one of the boxes of combs each year, usually the bottom box. The system is essentially the same as described previously but is often a little easier because when a double brood chamber colony is examined early in the season the queen will usually be found on a comb in the upper box. All that is then necessary is to slip a queen excluder between the two existing boxes and add the new box of combs or foundation on top. On this place a queen excluder followed by the supers. After three weeks the bottom box should be empty of brood and can be removed.

Colonies which are found to be weak after the winter should be examined carefully for disease. If they appear to be healthy, they should be united after discarding all but one of the queens. A honey surplus is more likely to be obtained from one strong colony rather than two of three weak ones.

In spring, bees require considerable quantities of water for preparing brood food from the stores in the combs. Water has to be carried by foragers from some local water supply. If there is no water reasonably near the hive, it is a good plan to help conserve their energy by providing a shallow pan of clean water in a sunny sheltered spot just far enough from the hive to avoid the droppings of other bees making cleansing flights. To prevent bees drowning it is a good idea to float some pieces of wood in the water, i.e. life rafts! The water in the pans must be topped-up regularly.

Summer Management

The main responsibilities of the beekeeper in the summer months are to ensure that the bees have sufficient room in the hive for the full development of the brood nest and for the storage of pollen and honey; he must be alert to the possibility of swarming; he must be ever watchful for signs of disease; and in agricultural areas he must be vigilant for signs of damage caused by toxic chemical sprays.

Swarming is encouraged if a colony is over-crowded in a small hive. It is important, therefore, to provide extra space in a hive a short time before it is actually needed, in other words, the beekeeper tries to anticipate colony needs and endeavours to keep one step ahead of the bees. This is often a difficulty for the novice since there is no denying that this type of knowledge only comes with experience. However, as a general rule another super should be added as soon as the bees have spread to occupy the outer frames of that on the hive. It should be noted that this critical point may be reached long before the combs are filled with honey. By these additions of supers the hive will grow in height during the summer, unless of course supers are removed from time to time for extraction. Because extracting honey can be a messy job, many beekeepers prefer to leave supers on the hives until August and then extract all their honey in one operation. Nowadays, this is only practical for suburban beekeepers and for those in rural areas where oil seed rape is not grown. In those arable farming areas where oil seed rape is cultivated it is necessary to extract honey which accrues from this crop as soon as possible after it is sealed in the combs because it can granulate so very quickly whilst still in the hive. The early flowering of the crop means that extraction is usually required in May or early June. The problems posed by oil seed rape are dealt with in more detail in a later chapter.

Honey can be removed and extracted during the season as required, providing it is fully capped, and adequate stores are left on the hive. It must always be remembered that British weather is notoriously changeable and unreliable and the bees may, therefore, need the honey they collected in May to see them through a wet June and July!

May, June and July are the common months for swarming in this country. The timing varies from year to year and from district to district. It appears to be more prevalent when an early spring allows stocks to become very strong early in the season. If a spell of bad weather ensues in May, swarming can be particularly troublesome as soon as the weather improves again. It seems possible that the crowding of the brood chamber when the bees are confined to the hive by bad weather may be the stimulus which triggers the swarming impulse. Because there are numerous methods advocated for swarm control, the astute reader will deduce that not any one of them is perfect. A widely used method which gives good results is described in **Chapter 6**.

In the south of England the main nectar flow usually occurs in the latter part of June and during July; by the first week of August it is normally over. After the flow is over the honey should be left on the hive for ten days or so to ensure that as much as possible is fully ripened and capped. Furthermore, some colonies become very aggressive when the flow ceases so it is wise to leave them alone for a short while to let them settle down.

The dates referred to above relate to the nectar flow which comes from the common flowers of summer such as white clover, brambles, willowherb, lime trees etc. and not, of course, to moorland heather which blossoms much later. Working for delectable heather honey is a special technique in which hives are taken to the moors in August and brought back in September.

CHAPTER 6

SWARMING

A swarm of bees in May
Is worth a load of hay;
A swarm of bees in June
Is worth a silver spoon;
But a swarm in July
Is not worth a fly.

Honeybees are social insects which, by definition, means that they live in colonies. Although individual members of a colony have very short life spans they are replaced as they die by young bees which are being reared most of the year. Theoretically, therefore, by this perpetual replacement of its losses, the honeybee colony as a unit should go on for ever. In reality, however, the colony is not immortal because disease, predators, fires etc. can all bring about its demise. Nature, therefore, requires that colonies should be able to multiply in number to provide replacements for those that perish. This is achieved by colony division into two or more independent viable units, when seasonal environmental conditions are favourable for their survival. Such activity is described as swarming. Not all colonies swarm every year. Modern beekeepers prefer strains of bees which have a low swarming tendency and by selective breeding try to encourage this trait.

From the beginning of May, in a prosperous stock, drones will begin to appear. This is normal and indicates that the stock is following the natural pattern of spring development. It does not mean that swarming is imminent but it should be taken as the first sign that the colony is developing in such a way that swarming may occur later. From then on, the beekeeper should inspect the brood chamber at intervals of not more than ten days. The sure sign that a stock intends to swarm is the building of queen cells. As described in an earlier chapter these, when fully developed, are distinctive acorn-shaped cells about 1 $\frac{1}{4}$ inches long which hang vertically from the combs. In a single brood box hive they are usually around the periphery of combs i.e. near the top bars, down the sides and along the bottoms. In a double brood box hive they are most frequently concentrated along the bottoms of the combs in the top box and along the tops of the combs in the bottom box.

In the early stages of development a queen cell is nothing more than a cup-shaped receptacle, very similar in appearance to the 'cup' which holds the acorn of the oak tree, but smaller in size. Its opening faces downwards. Most strong colonies will produce a number of these 'queen cups' during the season and by themselves do not necessarily indicate that swarming is imminent. If however they contain an egg or larva they are then true queen cells, with all that that implies. Sometimes a colony will start queen cells and then for some reason will abandon the impulse to swarm and destroy the cells. However, for all practical purposes, the presence of queen cells or cups in which there are eggs or larvae indicates that swarming is imminent. This is a reliable rule when the queen cells are numerous in the swarming season in a strong stock. There are, however, other circumstances in which a colony will build queen cells. If, for example, a queen is accidentally killed in a clumsy manipulation of a hive, the bees will quickly realise their loss and start emergency queen cells within a few hours. Clearly, these cells are for the purpose of replacing the lost queen and are not an indicator of swarming. Emergency queen cells can usually be recognised because they originate from worker cells in the brood frame, tending to protrude from the face of the comb curving downwards and do not have the straight vertical acorn shape of a queen cell built from a previously formed queen cup.

Another circumstance when queen cells may be formed is when a colony becomes alerted to the incipient failure of its queen through age, disease or some other defect. Because a vigorous queen is vital to a colony, measures are soon taken to replace any ailing matriarch by building queen cells from which a successor will later emerge. When this young queen is mated and proven to be fertile to the satisfaction of the colony, the old queen will be eliminated. This process in which a colony replaces its queen without swarming is termed supersedure. Sometimes the old queen is not eliminated immediately by her daughter and the two may co-exist in the same brood nest without apparent antagonism for a while, but eventually the old queen will disappear.

Very often queen supersedure occurs in a colony without the beekeeper being aware that it is taking place. Sometimes, the fact that it has happened is recognized when the beekeeper realises that the appearance of the queen has changed from that noted during previous colony inspections. For example, the old queen may have been marked and of light colour, whereas the new queen is seen to be unmarked and perhaps of different size and colouration.

A swarm settling on a tree

When queen cells are found in a colony it is important to decide whether they indicate the imminence of swarming or supersedure because these two quite different colony activities require completely different responses from the beekeeper. Although it is not possible to make dogmatic rules to differentiate with absolute certainty by simple inspection the impulse which has caused a colony to produce queen cells, there are, nevertheless, some very helpful clues. For example, if a colony comes through the winter strong in numbers, prospers well in a mild spring and becomes very populous by the end of May or early June and then builds a dozen or more queen cells it would be an almost certain bet that it is about to swarm. On the other hand, if a colony is of only moderate strength and only two or three queen cells are discovered it is then very probable that supersedure is taking place. The following table summarizes the features which, hopefully, will help the novice identify the cause of queen cells when they are discovered in a hive.

Let us now consider what happens when a colony is allowed to complete the natural activity of swarming without any interference from the beekeeper. In May or June, depending on seasonal weather conditions, a well developed populous colony will start to build queen cells. There may be a dozen or more. The contained larvae will be nourished on copious quantities of brood food (Royal Jelly) until the cells are capped on the ninth day after the egg was laid. At about this time, or a few days before, the diet of the old queen will have been restricted by the workers so as to curtail the activities of her ovaries and thereby make her slim and able to fly. Then, on a fine day soon after the queen cells are sealed, swarming will occur, usually between the hours of 10 am and 4 pm.. In a matter of a few minutes there will appear a surging mass of bees around the hive entrance and the air will become full of bees swirling around in all directions. The noise of the flying bees will be quite considerable and the whole spectacle will give the impression that the bees are in a state of ecstatic excitement. In a few minutes it will be seen that a cluster of bees is beginning to form on a branch of a nearby tree, or on a post or similar object not far from the hive. This will be where the old queen has settled after leaving the hive. Very soon the whole swarm will settle to cluster with the queen and it is then that the beekeeper has the best opportunity to collect them. This first swarm which leaves a hive and accompanies the old queen is usually referred to as a prime swarm and may contain half the population of the hive from which it emanated. It is usually good tempered and easy to handle because before leaving the hive the workers will have provisioned themselves by filling their honey stomachs with honey from the hive stores. When full of food bees are usually contented and unaggressive.

If the cluster is conveniently positioned on a low branch of a tree or bush all that is required is to hold a box or skep under it and by shaking the branch, or by striking the branch sharply with the hand, dislodge the cluster into the container. Alternatively, if the branch is thin it can be severed with garden pruners. As soon as the cluster is in the container cover it with a cloth and place it on the ground beneath the position from which the swarm was taken. The skep, or box, should then be inverted on the cloth with one edge raised by resting it on a stone or a piece of stick. This gives an entrance for the bees. If the procedure has gone successfully and the queen was dislodged into the container with the cluster, the majority of the bees will remain in the receptacle on the ground and after a while the flying bees will be seen to make their way down to join them. If, however, the queen is not in the container it will soon be deserted and the bees will rejoin her wherever she has taken refuge. When the cluster has reformed the whole exercise is repeated, bearing in mind that the objective is to get the queen into the container, in the knowledge that when this is achieved the rest of the swarm will soon join her.

When the swarm has safely settled in the box, or skep, on the ground, it should be left undisturbed in that position until the evening. Meanwhile, a hive should be prepared for its permanent accommodation. A floor, brood chamber with frames fitted with foundation, cover

	IMPULSE CAUSING QUEEN CELLS TO BE BUILT		
	SWARMING	EMERGENCY	SUPERSEDURE
TIME OF YEAR	Swarming season May to July	Anytime but especially after clumsy inspection	Anytime in the active season
COLONY CONDITION	Strong, populous	Any size	Often moderate or small size
PRESENCE OF QUEEN	May be present or may have left with swarm	Absent	Present
NUMBER OF QUEEN CELLS	6 to 20 or more	6 to 20 or more	Usually less than 6
POSITION OF QUEEN CELLS	Around edges of comb	Usually on face of comb	Usually lower centre of comb
APPEARENCE OF QUEEN CELLS	Vertical, acorn shape, hanging clear of comb	Built from worker cells. Closely attached to comb along vertical axis	Vertical, acorn shape, hanging clear of comb

Identifying features of the impulses causing queen cell production board, feeder and roof will be required. The hive should be sited in its permanent position, with the entrance wide open. Pieces of wood can be positioned so as to form a gentle incline from the ground up to the hive entrance. The wood should then be covered with part of an old, clean, bed sheet of sufficient size to cover a couple of square yards of ground in front of the hive. The objective of all this is to form an unobstructed uphill approach to the hive entrance.

In the evening, about an hour or so before dusk, the swarm in its container should be collected and brought to the hive. Holding the container over the sheet, quickly turn it upside down and with a firm shake or jerk, throw all the bees on to the centre of the sheet. A few bangs on the bottom of the inverted container will dislodge any remaining bees. Having done that you will then be privileged to watch one of the most fascinating and satisfying spectacles of beekeeping! Some bees will, of course, fly around, but the vast majority will remain on the sheet. They have a natural tendency to walk upwards and very soon some will enter the hive and begin to explore. These scouts will quickly ascertain that the hive is a suitable home and will encourage the rest of the swarm to follow. The message to enter the new-found home is passed by scent. If the entrance of the hive is carefully scrutinized when the bees begin to enter, a number of bees will be observed with their heads down, facing into the hive, their abdomens raised and wings beating vigorously. Near the tip of the abdomen a small white area may be visible. This is the Nasanov scent gland. By fanning air over this gland, an attractant scent is dispersed into the atmosphere which functions as a homing directional guide for the swarm. Within a short time it will become apparent that there is a general movement of the mass of bees upwards into the hive. Once this general movement starts, it is surprising how quickly the whole swarm disappears into the hive. By careful observation it is often possible to spot the queen as she enters.

Swarms are excellent comb builders and within a few hours the foundation in the frames will begin to be drawn into combs and in a day or two the queen will begin to lay eggs. The secretion of wax and comb building requires much energy which is derived from the consumption of food. Clearly, the only food possessed by a swarm in a new hive is that which the workers were able to bring with them in their honey stomachs. Although foragers will start to collect pollen and nectar remarkably quickly, this is dependent on weather conditions and there is always some risk, therefore, that the demand for food may out-strip the supply. For this reason a swarm should always be fed within a day or two of being hived. The food that is given is sugar syrup. This is made by dissolving white granulated sugar (NOT brown or any other sort!) in clean water, at a concentration of two pounds of sugar in each pint of water. The easiest way to prepare is to boil the water and then slowly stir in the sugar, making sure that the sugar does not burn on the bottom of the receptacle. Allow to cool and feed to the bees when lukewarm. At least a gallon of this syrup should be fed in the critical first week. By the end of this time, if weather conditions are good and there is a nectar flow, the foundation in all the frames in the brood box will be drawn into combs. A super should then be put on the hive, above a queen excluder, in the hope that the nectar flow will continue and honey will be stored. In a good season an early swarm will produce a little surplus for the beekeeper, but in the first season it is usually wise to forget about surplus honey and concentrate on building up a strong stock with adequate stores for the coming winter.

Having described the main features of a swarm, it is now appropriate to consider what happens in the hive from which a swarm issues. Immediately the swarm departs the population of bees in the hive is reduced by about a half; there will not be a queen present, but there will be a number of queen cells. Usually, there will be plenty of sealed brood and adequate reserves of food. Sixteen days from the time that the egg was laid in the queen cell, a virgin queen will emerge. This usually occurs a day or two after the swarm has left. When this young queen emerges there are two alternative courses of action she can follow. The first possibility is that she will seek out the other queen cells and kill her potential rivals before they can emerge. She will thereby become the sole heiress to the colony. This is the desirable outcome as far as the beekeeper is concerned. The alternative action of the young queen is that she may leave the hive with a second swarm. These small swarms containing virgin queens are called casts. Unfortunately, other queens when they emerge, may behave similarly and as a result the hive becomes depopulated by the issue of these numerous casts. This is something the beekeeper will wish to avoid, as he will be left with a weakened, unproductive unit. Casts can be difficult to retrieve because young virgin queens are good flyers with the irritating habit of flying far and high, perhaps finally settling in the top branches of trees!

Assuming that the first queen to emerge kills all her rivals, she is fed by the workers and in about five days becomes fully mature. Depending on the weather, she will take brief flights from the hive to familiarize herself with the surroundings and location of the hive. Usually, when between three and seven days old she begins her mating flights and in these mates with several drones, high in the air, sometimes more than 50 feet above the ground. It is believed that a queen may make several mating flights, copulating in total with a dozen or more drones until she has acquired sufficient sperm to last the rest of her life, because after these initial nuptials she never mates again. A few days after completion of mating she begins to lay eggs and the colony thereby becomes a viable unit. It is essential that a young virgin queen mates within her first three weeks of life, because after that time she is incapable of being properly impregnated and ends up as a useless drone layer.

Prevention of Swarming

Swarming disrupts the foraging activity of a colony and also grossly reduces the complement of workers. Consequently, after swarming the ability of a colony to produce a surplus of honey is significantly reduced for the remainder of that season. Furthermore, because some people are frightened by bees, stray swarms may cause problems with neighbours, especially in suburban areas. For these various reasons a good beekeeper will make every effort to prevent colonies swarming.

Although it has been stated earlier that swarming is a natural and necessary requirement of social insects, it must be appreciated that the instinct is not equally strongly present in all members of the same species. Variation within the species always exists and is indeed the linchpin of the Darwinian theory of evolution. It should not be surprising, therefore, to realise that some strains of honeybees are less prone to swarm than others and the beekeeper can take advantage of this to minimize his difficulties by selectively breeding from, or purchasing, bees with a low swarming tendency. As a corollary, it should be patently obvious that if a beekeeper stocks his apiaries with stray swarms, collected indiscriminately, it is more than likely that he will suffer a high incidence of swarming because the bees he has so acquired have already clearly demonstrated that trait!

There is good evidence that colonies headed by young queens are less likely to swarm, so many beekeepers make it their policy to replace queens after two full seasons.

Another factor which appears to promote swarming is congestion of the brood chamber. It is therefore highly desirable to ensure that the queen has an adequate sized brood chamber and that liberal super space is always available for honey storage.

However, despite attention to all these important general measures which help to deter swarming, it has to be accepted that some colonies will not be discouraged. The beekeeper, therefore, requires a system of management which allows him to spot when a colony is preparing to swarm, and, furthermore, contingency plans are required for dealing with the problem should it occur.

There are numerous methods recommended for swarm control: the fact that there are so many should make it obvious that none is perfect. In this small book it would not be appropriate to attempt to review all the various methods which are available. Advice, therefore, will be limited to the description of one relatively simple technique for swarm control, not necessarily because it is the best in all circumstances but because it is a method which is usually effective in most hands.

In this recommended procedure the beekeeper is required to inspect the brood nest of the colony regularly at ten-day intervals throughout the swarming season, which in the south of England stretches from early May to the end of July. The purpose of these ten-day inspections is to look for queen cells. If these are discovered, the old queen must be found and the comb on which she is present removed from the hive. If there are any queen cells on this comb they should be carefully destroyed. This comb, with the old queen thereon, is then placed in the centre of a new brood box which contains drawn combs or frames of foundation. At this point the old brood chamber and floor should be lifted aside and relocated a yard or two away with its entrance pointing in a direction different from its original placement. A new floor is then placed on the stand of the old hive, facing the same way as the previous one, and on this is positioned the new brood box containing the old queen. A queen excluder is applied and any supers removed from the original hive can then be added and the hive closed with a cover board and roof. In summary, what has been achieved is that the old queen is now in a new brood box with only one frame of brood, no queen cells, plenty of space, together with the original honey supers. All the foragers that were out working whilst these manipulations were going on will naturally return to this hive, which is in the position to which they are accustomed, and not to the hive which has been moved aside.

Having completed this part of the procedure attention must now be given to the original brood chamber which has been relocated. All the combs in this box must be carefully examined and any sealed queen cells should be cut out and destroyed. Select two unsealed queen cells which contain larvae and plenty of royal jelly and are in a good position on the combs where they are unlikely to be damaged during manipulation. The top bars of the frames containing the chosen queen cells can be marked with drawing pins. All other queen cells should be destroyed. Close up the combs in the brood box gently adding a drawn comb, or a dummy frame to fill any empty space. If the brood combs contain plenty of food no further action is required but if there is a shortage of food in the combs then a slow feeder of sugar syrup should be given and replenished as required. The hive is then closed and left undisturbed. During the ensuing days all the old bees will leave this hive and return to the hive on the original site to which they had previously orientated. Only a very much numerically reduced colony of young bees will be left with the queen cells. After a further five days the combs can be carefully inspected again by which time the selected queen cells should be sealed. If that is confirmed, any other queen cells that may have been started should be destroyed. After this manipulation the hive should be reassembled and the colony left alone for the next three weeks, apart from replenishing the feeder. During this period of time, if the weather is good, a young queen should emerge, mate, and start laying. If, when you inspect the hive after three weeks, you find eggs and larvae, you can celebrate the fact that you have a new queen!

The obvious consequence of this method of swarm control, if all has gone according to plan, is that the beekeeper has two queen-right colonies whereas previously he had one. A decision, therefore, has to be taken whether to continue with two stocks or revert back to one. If the requirement is for only one colony, then the hive containing the young queen should be moved about a foot each day towards that containing the old queen until the two hives are side by side and just about touching. At this time the old queen is removed from her hive and disposed of and the two colonies united using the newspaper method which is described in the following chapter. With a new young queen the colony is most unlikely to make any further attempt to swarm that season.

Even with the most well-tried method things do not always go according to plan. In the swarm control procedure which has been described the problem which occasionally arises is that when the new colony is inspected after three weeks, no eggs or larvae can be found. The explanation may be that a young queen has not emerged, or has been lost on a mating flight, but the beekeeper should not jump to this conclusion immediately because sometimes, when poor weather prevails, mating is delayed and egg laying may also be postponed. If no brood can be seen at this first inspection it is advisable to give a feed of sugar syrup in a slow feeder and inspect again after a further week. More often than not brood will be found at this second inspection, but if it is not, it is then reasonable to conclude that the colony is queenless and it should be united with the stock containing the old queen.

CHAPTER 7

UNITING AND QUEEN INTRODUCTION

A s indicated in the previous chapter, uniting colonies may be required following swarm control procedures. There are also other circumstances when this manipulation is necessary, or can usefully be employed. For example, it may be found in an apiary that one or more colonies are very small, the bees covering just a few combs in the brood chambers. Because weak colonies are not profitable and may perish in a harsh winter, something should be done to correct that unsatisfactory state. Providing the bees are healthy, the logical thing to do is to unite, in the knowledge that one strong colony is capable of producing a honey surplus, whereas a collection of small stocks will never do so.

Two small colonies can usually be united into a single brood chamber without much difficulty. The unwanted queen in one of the colonies is first removed and the bees and combs in both lots are then lightly sprinkled with flour, or sprayed with dilute sugar syrup. A small sprayer which delivers a fine mist is very convenient for this latter purpose. When the bees have been treated in this way all the combs can be put together in one box, alternating the combs of one colony with those from the other.

Uniting strong colonies, or amalgamating a weak lot with a strong colony, can be more difficult and has to be done slowly and carefully. The simplest way is that known as the 'newspaper method'. In this the unwanted queen is first removed from the colony which is to be added to another. The crown board, or queen excluder and supers if these are in use, of the receiving colony are removed and two sheets of newspaper placed upon the brood box. Most beekeepers think it helpful to make a couple of holes through this paper with a very fine nail. The brood box containing the queenless colony is then placed on top of that containing the queenright colony, the newspaper separating the two boxes. In this manipulation it is important to lower the top box into position carefully and accurately, because propolis will make it difficult to reposition without tearing the paper. The paper must be kept intact because it must function as a temporary barrier between the two colonies. By the time the bees have chewed through the paper the colony odours will have become mixed and the bees will then accept each other without fighting. It is best to carry out uniting in the evening when most of the foragers are in their respective hives. Evidence that successful uniting has occurred will be a pile of tiny newspaper fragments outside the hive entrance the next morning and no excessive number of dead bees! After uniting in this way the bees should not be disturbed for about a week. The combs in the two boxes can then be sorted and rearranged to form a compact brood nest flanked by combs containing stores. One box can be removed if all the bees and brood, together with combs of stores, can be accommodated in a single box without overcrowding.

Swarms can usually be united easily by putting them together in a single brood box and sprinkling the lot with flour or dilute sugar syrup. It is of interest that if two swarms emerge in an apiary at the same time they are quite likely to unite and cluster together without quarrelling.

Introducing a new queen into a colony is a fairly common requirement in practical beekeeping. For example, many beekeepers believe that queens deteriorate after two full seasons and, therefore, make it their policy to replace queens every two years. Sometimes a queen is accidentally killed in a clumsy hive manipulation and a replacement has to be introduced. Occasionally, a colony develops unpleasant aggressive tendencies and it becomes necessary to replace its queen with one from a docile strain. For these, and other reasons, it is highly desirable that a beekeeper is competent in the techniques of queen introduction.

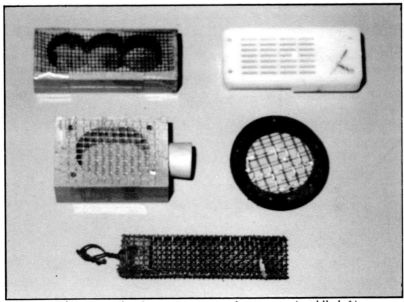

Queen mailing cages (top), temporary confining cage (middle left), queen marking cage (middle right), Butler introducing cage (bottom)

Before attempting to introduce a new queen, the first essential is to be sure that the receiving colony is queenless. Inexperienced beekeepers sometimes assume that a colony is queenless when, in fact, an undetected virgin queen is in the hive and are disappointed when a new valuable queen is not accepted. As a general rule, colonies are most easily re-queened in the spring and autumn; they tend to be most difficult in mid summer when they are very populous. A colony which is short of food is not in the best condition to accept a new queen, so it is always wise to feed prior to the introduction if stores are not adequate and there is no nectar flow.

An actively laying young queen in a nucleus colony is usually readily accepted. If such is available, all that is required is to remove the old queen from the colony to be re-queened and 12-24 hours later unite the nucleus to it using the newspaper method.

Although it is an advantage if young queens can be obtained from a local beekeeper who has reliable stock, it is very probable that the majority of hobbyists make their purchases from specialist breeders or suppliers, who may be some distance away. When obtained from these sources the queens are sent through the post in special small mailing cages. The conventional mailing cage is made from a small oblong piece of wood which is drilled out to give five sides of a box. The open side is then covered with fine wire mesh to complete the container. A hole is bored through each end. One of these is filled with sugar-candy and sealed over with a piece of card. The other end is plugged with a cork. Mailing cages made of plastic have come into use in recent years but the principles of use are much the same as with the conventional type. The queen is sent in the cage accompanied by about a dozen young workers. The mailing cage is also intended to act as an introducing cage. When used for this purpose the cage is placed between the brood frames of the recipient queenless colony, in the centre of the brood nest near young brood, after first removing the card covering the candy. In 24 hours or so, the bees will eat through the candy and release the queen. Whilst awaiting release in this way, the queen acquires the odour of the colony and it is presumed that this facilitates her acceptance.

The above method, although frequently used, has been criticised because it is claimed that the presence of attendant bees increases the risk of the queen being rejected. Furthermore, there is also the danger of introducing disease such as nosema, which may be present in the attendants. If these bees are carriers of disease and have been confined in the cage for several days it must also be assumed that the container will be contaminated. For these reasons it is recommended that a queen should be transferred to a new introducing cage, without attendants, before being given to a healthy colony.

When introducing a queen without attendants, it is essential that the bees to which she is being introduced should be able to feed and groom her. The mesh on the conventional mailing cage is too fine to allow this and it is, therefore, recommended that a cage made from $\frac{1}{8}$ inch wire mesh should be used, as advocated by the late Dr. C. Butler of Rothamsted.

It is desirable to introduce a queen to her new colony as soon as possible after receipt but sometimes this may not be convenient. If the manipulation has to be deferred for a day or two, the cage should be unpacked so that there is free ventilation through the wire mesh. If the bees have been confined for some while, two or three small drops of water can be placed on the mesh which the bees will take if they are thirsty. Until required the cage should be placed in a safe, cool place, such as a well ventilated cupboard.

The first step in the introducing procedure is to place the mailing cage containing the queen and attendants on its side close to the open feed hole of the recipient colony, after making that colony queenless. Do not remove the card covering the candy of the cage and do not remove the cork plug. Leave the cage exposed to the bees in this way for 24 hours. This 'conditioning' improves the chance of successful introduction, especially of a queen that has been caged for a long time.

After this conditioning period the queen should be separated from the attendants and put into the introducing cage immediately before being placed in the hive. For the novice the simplest way to make this transfer is to open the mailing cage in a closed room near a shut window. The attendant workers will soon come out, followed a little more cautiously by the queen. She can then be picked up and put in the cage, or gently coaxed into it whilst holding the cage entrance against the window. An alternative method is to open one end of the cage towards the light of a window in a closed room and allow the bees to come out, placing the entrance to the introducing cage over the hole when the queen is seen to enter the tunnel. Whatever method is used, care and patience are required because it must be remembered that young queens not in lay are liable to take wing.

When the queen is in the introducing cage, the open end should be covered with a single thickness of newspaper which is held in place with a rubber band. Because the queen is now without food or attendants the cage should be placed immediately in the hive, between the combs in the centre of the brood nest.

The above method of introducing a queen will probably be successful if the receiving colony is small, especially in the spring or autumn. It is not the method to be recommended, however, if the receiving colony is large, as may be found in the middle of summer. In these circumstances it is safest to effect the introduction in two stages. The first step in this method is to make a nucleus by taking three or four combs from the brood chamber of the colony to be re-queened, making sure that the old queen is not on these combs. Two combs should contain brood, preferably sealed, and well covered with bees. The other two combs should contain food. Place these combs in a nucleus box next to the hive being re-queened, but with the entrance facing in a different direction. Shake into the nucleus some more bees from another frame from the parent hive, again making sure that the old queen is not on the frame selected. Reduce the entrance to the nucleus to about half an inch and plug this loosely with a wisp of grass. Twelve to twenty-four hours later, the new queen in the introducing cage can be placed between the combs. Feed with sugar syrup through a slow feeder, replenishing as necessary, but do not otherwise disturb for a week. If the bees have not already done so after 24 hours, the wisp of grass blocking the entrance should be removed. After a week the nucleus can be inspected with the hope of finding that the new queen has been accepted and has started to lay. It is worth delaying further action for a few more days until a good sized patch of unsealed worker brood is visible. The old queen can then be removed from the parent colony and the nucleus re-united with it, using the newspaper method. Although this two stage method of queen introduction using a nucleus may seem slow and involves a little more work, it is strongly recommended because it is easily the most successful technique for the novice.

CHAPTER 8

FOOD SOURCES OF THE BEE

Honeybees satisfy their food requirements from nectar, honey dew, pollen and water. Nectar is essentially a solution in water of a number of sugars together with trace amounts of other substances which includes proteins, salts and aromatic materials. The precise composition of nectar varies with the plant species from which it is derived. It is produced in flowers by special organs called nectaries which are most frequently located at the base of the petals. Some plants, however, such as the Cherry Laurel, have nectaries which are quite divorced from flowers, being found on the leaves and stems. Such nectaries are described as 'extra-floral'. In most nectar the predominant sugar found is sucrose, a disaccharide, together with lesser quantities of the monosaccharides, glucose and fructose. However, an exception to this generalization is found in the group of plants known as the Cruciferae. This group is of great importance to beekeepers because it includes such species as oilseed rape, charlock, etc.. The nectar from these plants contains only glucose and fructose, but not in equal proportions, glucose predominating. This has significant consequences because the high ratio of glucose to fructose influences the physical properties of the honey which results. Honey containing a high proportion of glucose to fructose will granulate very quickly, whilst that containing an excess of fructose will granulate only slowly.

In the process of conversion of nectar to honey, sucrose is broken down to the simpler sugars, glucose and fructose. This is effected by the enzyme invertase which is secreted by the glands in the head of the bee and added to the nectar as it is collected. Nectar, as secreted by the plant, may contain 60% water. Much of this has to be removed in its conversion to honey, which should contain less than 20% water. This is done in the hive through much hard work by the bees.

On entering the hive the returning forager passes her nectar load to the house bees by opening her mandibles and regurgitating drops of nectar from her honey crop on to the proboscis. The house bees take this offered food, adding further enzymes, and manipulating the nectar between their mouth parts and probosci so as to expose a large surface area from which water can evaporate. The elimination of water is helped by the warmth in the brood nest area (34-35 °C/93-95 °F) and the circulation of air through the hive by other house bees fanning with their wings. The incoming nectar is passed freely between the house bees and the water content of the nectar may be reduced below 40% in a few hours. Further reduction of water content occurs by evaporation from the open cells of the honeycomb into which the unripe honey is deposited. In good summer weather and with good hive ventilation, nectar may be converted into honey and sealed in the combs in less than a week. When conditions are not ideal it may take much longer. Sometimes during a heavy nectar flow, if the nights are cool, water vapour vented from the hive during the night condenses on the alighting board, and can be seen as a wet patch in the early morning.

Honeydew is a sweet substance excreted by populations of small plant sucking insects, which include aphids. These insects are adapted to penetrate plant tissues with special feeding tubes, or bristles, through which they gain access to the plant sap. From this they extract the nutriments they require whilst the remainder of the sap is passed through their alimentary tract to be deposited on the surface of the plant. This deposit is a complicated substance containing sucrose, fructose, glucose, higher sugars, amino acids, organic acids and salts. It is attractive to bees, especially when good nectar sources are not available. Honeydew honey is usually dark in colour and strongly flavoured.

Nectar and honeydew provide carbohydrates (i.e. sugars etc.) for the bees' nourishment but, by themselves, are not an adequate diet. For the rapid tissue building which occurs in the growth of young larvae, liberal quantities of proteins are also necessary. These essential proteins are

Pussywillow (Salix Caprea) a good source of spring pollen

obtained from pollen which is collected from flowers by the foragers. It has been estimated that a strong colony of bees may collect and use more than 100 lbs of pollen annually. This represents something like four million bee-loads of pollen! In addition to proteins, pollen also provides smaller quantities of vitamins, fats and minerals.

In the British Isles we are fortunate to have a wonderful mixed flora which provides pollen throughout most of the year. Some parts of the world are not so fortunate and in those areas beekeepers often resort to feeding their bees a pollen substitute consisting mainly of soya flour and brewers' yeast.

In the U.K., because of the early flowering of oilseed rape, some beekeepers have found it helpful to encourage the early spring development of colonies by feeding pollen supplements. For this purpose, in those periods of the season when there is a glut of pollen producing plants, beekeepers take advantage of this to harvest pollen for use at a later date. This can be achieved by fitting a special pollen trap to the hive entrance to strip a proportion of the pollen loads from the bees legs as they enter. After collection it is stored in small bags in a deep freezer to be used when required. It is usually prepared as a patty, a popular recipe being three parts soya flour, one part pollen, two parts white sugar, and one part water. The ingredients are mixed into a stiff dough and fashioned into one pound patties, and placed on grease proof paper. The patties, with the paper underneath, are positioned on the top bars of the brood chamber in the spring, usually February and March. Once pollen patty feeding is started in the spring it must be continued until normal natural supplies of pollen are available.

Bees collect quantities of water from dew, raindrops, ponds, puddles, drains etc. They use it to dilute honey for food, to dissolve granulated honey, and in summer to cool the hive.

Bees will sometimes fly three or four miles to exploit a specially attractive food source but their most efficient foraging range is probably not more than 1 mile from their hives. They are selective in that they will direct their activities to plants offering the best quality and quantity of nectar, irrespective of whether these are cultivated crops or wild plants. For millions of years bees foraged on the natural wild flora and it is only in comparatively modern times in the developed world that cultivated food crops have come into their sphere of interest. In the densely populated British Isles, the environmental changes affecting the food sources of the honeybee have been enormous, especially in the last hundred years. If we look back to the last century, farm work was then entirely dependent on the horse, as was most transportation. Large acreages of fodder crops, which included clover and lucerne, were grown to feed the huge horse population. These crops were of benefit to bees. Fields in those times were small and surrounded by hedges. The crops which were grown were often invaded by numerous flowering weeds because herbicides were not available. Chemical pesticide sprays were unknown. Artificial fertilizers supplying nitrogen were not available and soil condition had to be maintained by organic manures and rotation of crops, the latter including clover for its nitrogen fixing ability. In those times beekeeping prospered in the rural areas as a source of supplementary income for farm labourers and cottagers.

Today all is changed! Farming is mechanized and there are no working horses and consequently fodder crops are only grown in much reduced quantities for other animals. In the last 50 years hedgerows have disappeared at a rate of more than 2,000 miles each year. Approximately 95% of hay meadows, 80% of chalk downland, 60% of heathland, 50% marshes, and 40% natural woodland have all been lost! Weeds no longer flourish in cultivated crops through the use of potent herbicides and both pests and beneficial insects, including bees, are assaulted with chemical pesticides. In the light of all these developments it is not surprising that some parts of the arable farming areas of the country have been likened to deserts, in so far as beekeeping is concerned! They also help to explain why suburban beekeepers usually produce more honey than those in rural areas.

However, all is not gloom in the arable farming areas because in the last twenty five years some new crops have been introduced which are beneficial to bees. There is also a growing movement to discourage very intensive farming practices and, in addition, there is an increasing consumer demand for organically grown foods.

The most important new nectar producing crop which has been cultivated extensively in the U.K. in the last twenty five years is oilseed rape. Although the crop has been known for some hundreds of years and grown in small quantity, it was not until the European Economic Community used their intervention procedures to encourage the crop that farmers became seriously interested. The amount grown has since escalated dramatically. Up to 1972 about 6,000 hectares were grown annually whereas today the crop is more than 400,000 hectares! The great significance of this for the beekeeper is that oilseed rape produces nectar profusely when conditions are right. It has been estimated that

A comb with stored pollen on left; honey on right

under ideal conditions one hectare of the crop could produce well over 100 kg of honey! In practice it is not possible to harvest the full crop potential, largely because it flowers early in the year when honeybee colonies are not fully developed and because of fickle spring weather conditions in the U.K.. However, if only one third of the potential honey crop was realized this would amount to some 12,000 tonnes of honey! The significance of this quantity can be appreciated when it is related to honey production in the U.K. which in recent years has averaged between 1,000 and 3,0000 tonnes annually.

Currently the oil from crushed rapeseed is mostly used by the food industry. Clearly, as E.E.C. production targets for food requirements are achieved, subsidies will be withdrawn and the crop will become less financially attractive to farmers. For this reason it has already been suggested that the U.K. acreage of the crop is unlikely to expand much further. However, research in a number of European countries has recently demonstrated that rapeseed oil can be processed to become usable in diesel engines. Furthermore, it is claimed that the new fuel is more environmentally friendly than Derv! With the technology available for the production of this bio-diesel fuel it seems likely, therefore, that demand for it will increase as fossil fuel reserves are depleted. Perhaps farmers will again be encouraged to increase acreages, to the advantage of beekeepers.

In some parts of the country small lots of unusual crops such as borage, lupins, flax, lavender, evening primrose, and sunflowers are being grown to special order, or experimentally, but they are only of significance to those beekeepers with hives in the immediate vicinity.

Common Bee plants of the United Kingdom

Those marked * provide pollen only.

1. Major nectar and pollen sources.

**February/
March**   Nil

April   Plum, Cherry, Pear, Oilseed rape.

May   Apple, Dandelion, Hawthorn, Sycamore, Oilseed rape

June   Sainfoin, Broad Beans, Raspberry, White clover, Blackberry

July   Bell heath, Blackberry, Limes, White clover, Willowherb

August   Bell heath, Red clover, Willowherb, Ling heather, Mustard

**September/
October**   Ling heather, Mustard

2. Minor nectar and pollen sources.

February/
March Laurustinus, Winter Heath, Snowdrop, Alder*, Hazel*, Crocus, Elm*, Poplar*, Gorse, Yew*, Willow, Coltsfoot, Blackthorn, Prunus, Almond, Celandine, Wood Anemone*

April Box, Aubretia, Ash*, Berberis, Dead nettle, Maples, Currants, Gooseberry, Crab apple, Laurel

May Wallflower, Forget-me-not, Brassicas, Beech*, Bluebell, Birch*, Horsechestnut, Cotoneaster, Oak*, Holly, Plantain*, Broom

June White Bryony, Wild rose, Elder*, Rock rose*, Charlock, Bilberry, Robinia, Thyme, Yellow Melilot, Cranesbill, Asparagus, Red clover, Birdsfoot trefoil, Bindweed, Vipers burgloss

July Poppy*, Campanulas, Veronicas, Cornflower, Privet, Knapweed, Hogweed, Borage, White Melilot, Mignonette, Knotgrass, Scabious, Meadowsweet*, Sweet chestnut, Mullein, Figwort, Mallow

August Balsam, Borage, Chicory, Dwarf gorse, Fuchsia, Golden rod, Helenium, Knotgrass, Mallow, Marjoram, Meadowsweet*, Michaelmas daisy, Mint, Mullein, Sunflower, Purple loosestrife, Sage, Scabious, Sea lavender, Snowberry, Thistle, Toadflax, Travellers Joy, Virginia creeper, White charlock, White Melilot

September/
October Balsam, Dwarf gorse, Fuchsia, Ivy, Michaelmas daisy, Sea lavender, Thistle, White charlock.

CHAPTER 9

COMMUNICATION IN THE COLONY

I n the previous chapter the important natural food sources of the honeybee were described. The fascinating questions that must now be addressed concern the remarkable ability of a forager, having found a rewarding source of food, to navigate its way quickly back to the hive, deposit its load and return without difficulty to the site it found fruitful. Furthermore, once a good food source is discovered it is soon obvious that the number of bees exploiting it increases rapidly, suggesting that the successful forager is able to communicate to other foragers the whereabouts of a good food supply. These remarkable abilities of the honeybee can be illustrated by a simple field experiment.

If a container of strong sugar syrup, or honey, is placed on open ground about 50 yards from a colony of bees, it may be some while before it is fortuitously discovered by a scouting bee. Whilst this bee is taking the food, it can be marked on the thorax with a small blob of quick drying non-toxic paint. As soon as the bee has taken its fill it will depart, taking a straight flight line back to the hive. In a matter of a few minutes it will be back for more food, being identified by the blob of paint on the thorax. Very soon, other bees will begin to arrive, and in a short time there will be a host of bees collecting food from the container.

This simple experiment suggests that when a bee discovers a good food source it can return to it immediately without difficulty and, further-more, it can apparently recruit other members of the colony to help exploit the newly found food.

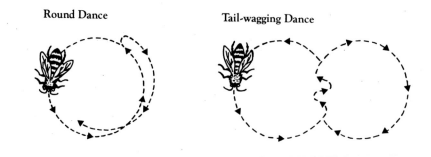

Round Dance

Tail-wagging Dance

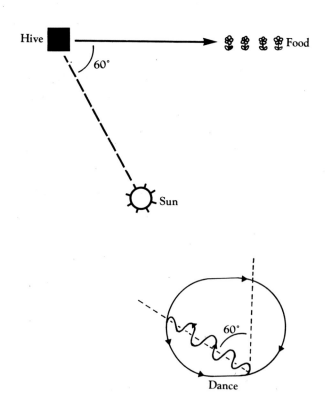

Hive

60°

Food

Sun

60°

Dance

Bee dances

The navigational methods which bees use to enable them to return to a food supply, and the way that information on the location of food is passed to other foragers, have been studied most brilliantly by Professor von Frisch. More than fifty years ago, von Frisch published details of his work in which he described how successful foragers could communicate the location of their supply to other bees in the hive by 'dancing' on the combs. Briefly, if a worker bee finds a good source of food, she will, on return to the hive, perform on the comb face, either a 'round dance' or a 'tail-wagging dance', the particular dance depending on the distance of the food from the hive. If the food is less than 80 metres away she performs a round dance, running around rapidly in a circle, alternating the directions of the circular movements. If the food is a greater distance away then the tail-wagging dance is used. The round dance can be interpreted as a message saying *"Go out of the hive; there is food close by"*. As far as is known no indication of the direction to fly is given but the smell of the blossom remaining on the dancers will give some intimation of the food source.

When food is some distance from the hive, information on the location of the food is obviously desirable so as avoid foragers wasting a vast amount of time and energy searching a wide area. The tail-wagging dance provides this information giving both the direction and the distance of the food. The rhythm of the dance indicates the distance: when food is near the dance cycles are done quickly with vigorous tail-wagging, whereas when food is a long way away the dance cycles are completed slowly and the tail-wagging appears sluggish. Directional information is conveyed by the tail-wagging part of the dance, the sun being used as the point of reference. On the vertical honeycomb in the dark hive, the angle between the direction of the sun and the food source is transposed by the forager into an angle with respect to gravity. For example, a tail-wagging run vertically up the comb means that the food lies in the direction of the sun, whereas a tail-wagging run straight down the comb means that the food is in the opposite direction to the sun. If the tail-wagging run is up the comb at an angle of 60° to the left of the vertical, the food is 60° to the left of the sun, and so on.

The 'dance' method of communication which has been described is a specific one with limited purpose; it is simply a technique for scout bees and foragers to indicate to other colony members the local whereabouts of something desirable, usually food, but it is also used during the act of swarming to signify the location of a suitable new home. Clearly, in the complicated structure and relationships found in colonies of social insects, there is a need to communicate to the individual members a wide variety of information, quite apart from that related to foraging. This is achieved by the release of chemical substances called pheromones. In simple terms, a pheromone can be described as a chemical agent which is secreted to the outside by an individual and when received by another of the same species induces a specific reaction. Many pheromones have been recognized in honeybees of which queen, alarm and Nasonov are perhaps the best known.

Queen pheromone is secreted by the mandibular glands of the mated queen and is dispersed over her body surface when she grooms herself. Workers lick it from her body and distribute it amongst themselves. The main effects of the pheromone is to promote the cohesion of the colony, suppress worker ovary development and inhibit queen rearing.

Alarm pheromones are produced by glands associated with the sting apparatus, and to a lesser extent by the mandibular glands, of worker bees. They are released when a colony is threatened or disturbed, their purpose being to alert the colony, mark the intruder to be attacked, and stimulate further stinging.

The Nasanov pheromone is secreted by a small gland (sometimes called the scent gland) which lies in a grove in the upper surface of the seventh abdominal segment of the worker. To release the scent the worker flexes the tip of the abdomen downwards and at the same time fans with her wings creating a flow of air over the gland to disperse the scent. The Nasanov pheromone is an attractant. Its use can be seen most vividly when a swarm is about to enter a new home. At that moment many workers will assemble around the entrance, facing towards it, heads down, abdomen flexed, fanning vigorously, with the small white gland visible on the top of the abdomen near the tip.

A number of other pheromones have already been identified, and undoubtedly many more await detection. For further information on these fascinating substances the reader is referred to specialist scientific texts which are available.

CHAPTER 10

THE HONEY HARVEST

It used to be common practice in the U.K. to leave all honey on the hive until the end of the main nectar flow, which usually occurs in late July or early August. Beekeepers with apiaries in suburban locations, and those in rural areas where there is no arable farming, may still conveniently continue this practice, but those in areas where oilseed rape crops are grown have been obliged to change. Rapeseed honey, and that from other flowering brassica crops, is liable to crystallize quickly if left more than a short time in the combs, making extraction impossible by the usual means. For that reason, such honey should be removed from the hive as soon as it is capped, and extracted at once. Because oilseed rape flowers and yields its nectar very early in the season, it becomes obligatory to extract the resulting honey crop in May or early June. Of necessity, a second extraction then has to be undertaken at the end of the summer to harvest honey arising from the main nectar flow.

Although beekeepers in oilseed rape areas are obliged to extract early for the reasons stated, it must be appreciated that if hives are denuded of all their surplus there is a risk of starvation if bad weather ensues and foraging is prevented. Colonies in early summer will be breeding strongly and have a high demand for food. If this is not immediately available they will starve remarkably quickly. The responsible bee-keeper should, therefore, always be alert to this possibility when removing honey in the early part of the season and be prepared to feed as necessary.

To remove a honey crop from a hive it is first necessary to separate the bees from the combs which are to be taken. In other words, to clear the bees from the honey supers so that when the latter are removed they are not crowded with bees. However, before this manipulation is attempted it is essential to inspect the super boxes carefully to make sure that there are no holes or defects through which robber bees can enter. When supers are cleared they are undefended and it is surprising how quickly robbers will exploit the situation if they can find a way in.

There are a number of methods for clearing bees from honey supers. Probably the simplest way for the novice is by means of a clearer-board. The usual clearer-board is nothing more than a standard crown-board with a Porter bee escape fitted into the feed hole. This escape can be likened to a one-way valve, allowing bees to pass down from the supers into the brood chamber but preventing their return. Porter escapes are available made in plastic or tinplate. Their essential mechanism con-

Left, a honey bottling tank. Right, a tangential extractor. The extractor shown has a pully for belt drive from an electric motor. For manual operation this is replaced by a handle

A twenty frame radial extractor

sists of two passages guarded by delicate springs through which the bees can pass in only one direction. The entrance to the escape is through a central round hole in the top and the two exits are below. Many crown-boards have a single feed hole and will, therefore, only accommodate one escape. This is not entirely satisfactory because it tends to make clearing slow and difficulties arise if this single route becomes blocked. It is much better to modify crown-boards so that they will accommodate two or three escapes.

When honey is to be removed from a hive, the supers are lifted off and the clearer board placed in position on top of the brood chamber, making sure that the entrances to the escapes are facing upwards. It is not essential to remove the queen excluder but many find it convenient to do so. Any brace comb which might obstruct the entrances or exits of the escapes must be removed. The honey supers are placed back on the hive, above the clearer board, the hive reassembled and finally, once again, carefully scrutinized to make sure there are no holes or defects through which robbers can enter.

The rate at which bees will clear from supers is very variable. It is quickest when the combs are fully sealed and slowest when there is unsealed honey present. If by some mischance there is brood in the supers the bees will certainly not leave. However, in normal circumstances, supers should clear in something like 48 or 72 hours.

As soon as the supers are free of bees they should be removed from the hive, taken from the apiary and placed in a warm, clean, bee-tight room or shed to await extraction. Ideally, combs should be extracted immediately, but if this is not possible they should be kept somewhere warm. If honey is allowed to get cold its viscosity increases and thereby becomes much more difficult to extract.

When it comes to extracting the honey the first question to be addressed is where to do it. If the honey you produce is entirely for your own consumption then any bee-tight accommodation will do if it satisfies your own standards of hygiene as a place suitable for the preparation of food.

However, and most importantly, if you intend to supply other people with honey for human consumption, either by gift or sale, then it must be handled and prepared under strict hygienic conditions as required by regulations authorized by the Food Safety Act (1990) which came into effect on 1st January, 1991. Up to the time of writing, it is not clear how many regulations will be introduced and how they will be applied to the small domestic producer. Nevertheless, it is laid down that Authorized Officers will have the right to inspect any premises where foodstuffs are prepared for sale, to examine the method of preparation and equipment used, to examine the end product, and to ensure that all these matters comply with the set standards. In brief, accommodation used for the preparation of foodstuffs should be clean and in good condition so that the food cannot be contaminated by dirt, germs, fungi, insects, vermin or odours. Clean water should be available for washing and food operators will be required to work hygienically. At the moment it appears that the average domestic kitchen will satisfy the requirements in so far as the small hobbyist producer is concerned. However, it must be emphasized that beekeepers should remain alert to possible future changes in the regulations which may affect their activities.

Probably the majority of hobbyist beekeepers will do their extracting in the kitchen and, because it tends to be a messy job, will wish to get it over quickly. If only a few supers have to be dealt with it is probably most convenient to remove them from the hives in early evening and extract immediately. The room to be used should be emptied as far as possible, except for the kitchen table. The floor can be covered with newspaper. The first task is to sort through the combs, separating those with fully sealed honey from those where it is not fully capped. The latter should be set aside together with any combs containing honey which has granulated. The best quality honey comes from fully sealed combs and

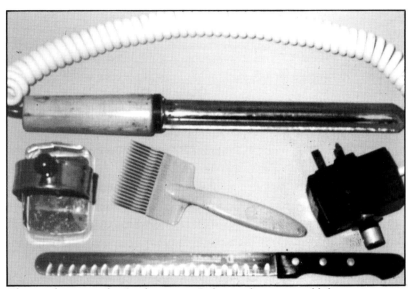

Electric decapping knife, decapping fork, comb cutter, cold decapping knife

it is, therefore, desirable to extract this first so that it does not become mixed with that of lower quality. If honey of a particular colour is required (i.e. light, medium or dark) the combs can be further sorted by holding the combs up to a bright light. Broad differences of colour can be detected by this means, providing that the comb wax is not old and dark. The batches of different coloured combs can then be extracted, starting with the light, followed by medium and ending with the dark. Before honey can be extracted from a comb the wax cappings on the cells have to be removed. A simple and efficient tool for this purpose is a long, stainless steel knife, with a very sharp hollow-ground cutting edge. Suitable knives can be obtained from suppliers of beekeeping equipment. The knife is used cold. More expensive and elaborate knives are available, such as those heated by steam or electricity, but these are not necessary for the hobbyist with only one or two hives. A large bowl or dish is required to catch the cappings as they are cut from the combs. It is convenient to place a piece of clean wood across the top of this receptacle on which the end of the frame can be rested whilst being uncapped.

The frame to be decapped should have any metal spacers removed and is then held vertically, the bottom end resting on the wood across the top of the cappings collecting receptacle. The knife is used with a sawing motion, trying to effect a shallow cut so that little more than cappings are detached. For safety it is usually recommended that the cutting direction should be downwards away from the holding hand at the top of the frame. Many beekeepers, however, find that they can control the knife better with an upward direction of cut. If this method is adopted great care must be taken to keep fingers away from the line of cut, just in case the knife slips off the comb! When both sides of a comb have been uncapped, it is then ready to be placed in the extractor.

The conventional honey extractor is essentially a cylindrical metal or plastic barrel containing a central rotor into which the uncapped combs are placed. The rotor is geared to a handle in small manual machines, or an electric motor in larger appliances. When the rotor is spun, honey is thrown outwards by centrifugal forces, hits the inside of the barrel and runs down to collect at the bottom. It is removed through a wide-bore tap.

All extractors use centrifugal force to remove honey from the combs but there are two different basic designs in which the positioning of the combs in the rotor is dissimilar. The design difference concerns the placement of the combs relative to the circle of rotation: in 'tangential machines' the combs are held in the tangential plane, whilst in 'radial machines' the combs are positioned radially,

The tangential extractor is well suited to manual operation and is commonly used by the small-scale honey producer. The machines are small, usually holding two, four or six super frames at each loading.

Decapping a comb

When a comb is placed in the rotor, one side will face outwards towards the barrel and the other will face inwards towards the spindle. The drawback of this arrangement is that when the rotor is spun only honey in the cells on the outward facing surface of the comb will be released, which means that the machine has to be stopped and the comb reversed in order to extract both sides. In practice, to avoid breaking combs heavy with honey, it is necessary to do two reversals. The combs are spun initially at slow speed, reversed and spun again at slow speed. This should remove the bulk of the honey and reduce the weight of the combs. After this, high speed can be used, but again the machine has to be stopped to reverse the combs to complete the extraction. Clearly, this need to reverse combs during extraction is acceptable when only small numbers are involved. It becomes tiresome and time consuming when a large work load is involved. For larger producers the radial machine is much more efficient. In this type the combs are placed in the rotor radiating from the centre spindle, like the spokes of a wheel, with the top bars to the outside. The great advantage of this arrangement is that both sides of the combs are extracted simultaneously and do not have to be reversed during extraction. Also, for a given diameter of extractor barrel, more combs can be accommodated radially than tangentially, popular radial models having a capacity of 20 or more combs at one loading. The disadvantage of the arrangement is that at equivalent speeds of rotation, honey leaves the combs slower than in the tangential types. To facilitate honey extraction in radial machines, therefore, greater centrifugal force has to be generated by higher rotational speeds. For that reason, most of these machines of larger size are power driven, usually by an electric motor.

The best extractors are made of stainless steel but to save cost some smaller models are available with food grade plastic barrels which, with care, are quite serviceable. However, there is much to be said for the more robust stainless steel machines. Extractors made of tinplate are not recommended as they are more difficult to clean and tend to rust along the seams and are unlikely to comply with standards which may be set by regulations under the Food Safety Act (1990).

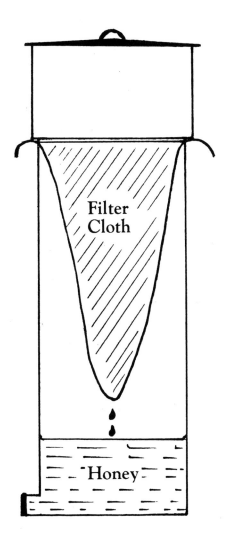

Illustrating the correct position for a filter cloth in a Bottling bank

Honey as it comes from the extractor contains pieces of wax, perhaps fragments of bees, and numerous air bubbles. Before it is bottled and fit for consumption it must be strained to remove the extraneous matter and allowed to settle in a warm place so that the air bubbles will rise to the surface. For this purpose a tall, cylindrical container made of stainless steel or food grade plastic is used, known as a bottling, or settling, tank. Various sizes are available between $1/2$ cwt and 2 cwt. capacity. In the top of the bottling tank is a removable wire mesh strainer which will sieve out larger pieces of wax and other foreign bodies. To filter out the tiniest particles of wax etc. it is necessary to pass the honey through a straining cloth of butter muslin, organdie, or 54 mesh to the inch Nylon cloth. This straining cloth is tied in position in the bottling tank below the wire mesh strainer as illustrated in diagram.

The normal procedure is to run the honey from the extractor into a clean 28 lb. food grade plastic honey pail, or similar receptacle, in order to transfer it to the bottling tank. It is then poured carefully into the top of the strainer which it will pass through, then on through the cloth below to drop into the tank. Although the honey will now be free from all foreign matter, it will contain numerous tiny air bubbles, giving it a rather cloudy appearance. If the tank is placed in a very warm room for about 48 hours, the air bubbles will rise to the top to form a froth which can be removed. When clarified in this way the honey is ready for bottling in the appropriate jars, or run into 28 lb. containers for storage in bulk.

When all the honey has been removed from the extractor and transferred to the bottling tank attention should be given to the receptacle containing the cappings which were cut from the combs. This will be found to contain quite a lot of honey which can be recovered by scooping it into the strainer on the bottling tank, together with the cappings, and allowing it to drain through into the tank.

The procedures which have so far been described relate to those combs of honey which were found to be fully sealed at the original sorting; in other words, the high quality part of the crop. It will be recalled that combs containing unsealed or granulated honey were put aside to be dealt with later. These will now be considered.

It is unlikely that all combs in a super will be fully capped. Indeed, most combs will have some unsealed cells but if these amount to less than 10% of the total they can be disregarded and the comb accepted as fully satisfactory. Combs which contain more than 10% unsealed honey must be examined carefully to ensure that the honey is ripe and of good viscosity. The easiest way to do this is to hold the comb in a horizontal position and submit it to a vigorous downward shake. If the honey is of good viscosity it will not leave the comb whereas if it is thin and watery it will shake out easily. Unsealed honey of good viscosity can be extracted and consumed but it should be segregated from the best quality product and used without great delay. Combs in which the honey is thin and watery should not be used. They are best given back to the bees.

Honey which has granulated in the comb cannot be extracted. It is a most tedious problem to deal with and patience is required! Perhaps the simplest approach is to cut out all the granulated combs from their frames and to chop them into small fragments in a bowl. This is then transferred to a 28 lb. tin which is placed in a heating cabinet at about 125 °F. After 24 hours the honey will have liquefied and can be poured out, to be filtered and bottled in the usual way. The remaining wax can be put in a feeder and given to the bees to clean.

Comb Honey

So far, only the harvesting of a crop of liquid honey has been described. Many beekeepers and consumers, however, consider that honey in the comb is to be preferred because it is claimed to have a better flavour than the extracted variety. Comb honey, therefore, commands a premium price and many beekeepers may wish to produce it.

In the past, beekeepers were expert at producing comb honey for sale in small 4 1/4 inch square frames made of thin bass wood known as sections. They weighed about 1 lb. and were much in demand. Undoubtedly, skilled management of the bees was required to produce good sections as also was abundant forage to give profuse nectar flows. Today, apart from bass wood, plastic and round section containers are also available. Although sections are still produced in the U.K. by enthusiasts the majority of beekeepers here market comb honey as portions cut from larger combs and described as 'cut comb'. This is really the modern alternative to sections and, as a delicacy, just as attractive.

To produce cut-comb honey, special thin unwired foundation is fitted into frames of a super and put on the hive when there is a good nectar flow. It must be noted, however, that no attempt should be made to produce comb honey when the bees are foraging on oilseed rape. The rapid granulation of honey from that crop makes it completely unsuitable. If possible, a super of cut-comb honey should be removed as soon as it is sealed otherwise the cappings may become a little discoloured by the constant movement of bees over them.

Heather Honey

Heather honey is a great delicacy which is only available to beekeepers who are fortunate enough to have apiaries near to moors where ling heather grows, or are prepared to transport their hives to the moors. Honey from ling heather is unique because it sets like a jelly but becomes liquid when stirred, a peculiar physical property which is described as thixotropy. This property makes for difficulty in extracting the honey in an extractor but it can be done if the honey in the comb is first agitated with a special implement. A variety of such implements have been introduced, one has a series of fine prongs which, after decapping the comb, are inserted into the cells and after some quick up and down movements to agitate, the honey becomes sufficiently mobile to be spun out in an extractor. Clearly, this is a time consuming process.

The more traditional way to release heather honey from the combs is by squeezing it out with a specially designed press. However, it has to be said that heather honey makes marvellous cut-comb and the small producer can avoid much labour by harvesting in this style.

CHAPTER 11

PREPARING AND PACKAGING HONEY FOR SALE

Newly extracted honey can be run into jars from the bottling tank after it has been allowed to settle for about 48 hours. It should then be clean, clear, attractive to the eye, and ready for consumption. Jars must be clean and dry and without cracks or other defects. Most beekeepers still prefer to use conventional 1 lb. (454 g) or 8oz (227 g) squat glass honey jars with lacquered metal lids but plastic containers are also available. When filling the jars, which must be done in a clean hygienic place, it is preferable that both the jars and the honey are warm. The packer must take every precaution to ensure that each jar contains the correct declared weight of honey. In the standard glass squat honey jar it is necessary to fill well above the jar shoulder up to the screw thread so that when the lid is in place it covers the level of the honey. No air space should, therefore, be visible in the top of the jar when it is standing on a level surface. Although this is a reasonable working guide that correct weight is given it does not obviate the fact that in law an item which is being sold by weight should be checked on properly certified trade equipment bearing the stamp of an Inspector of Weights and Measures, or an E.E.C. stamp.

Difficulties can arise when substantial quantities of honey have to be handled. If the total crop is put into jars at once it may not be possible to dispose of it all immediately and after a while the honey will become hazy and unattractive due to the start of granulation. Honey, as a clear liquid, or when fully granulated, is attractive, but at an intermediate stage between these two physical states has little appeal. The best policy, therefore, for those with a large crop is to store it in bulk in 28 lb. food grade plastic or tinplate containers in a cool place and bottle

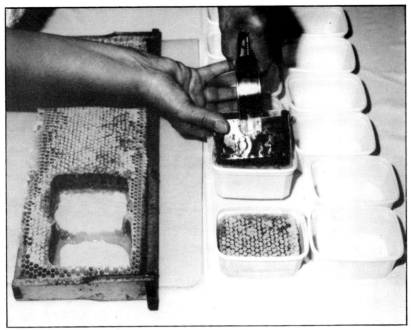

Using the Price comb cutter

for market as required. Tinplate containers are best used with a plastic liner to prevent the honey contacting rusty seams etc..

When a can of honey is withdrawn from store for use, the contents are inspected and if there is no evidence of granulation it can be warmed and transferred to the bottling tank and put into jars. If, however, on inspection, the honey is found to have set into a solid state, there are really two alternative ways to proceed. Both procedures require the use of a warming cabinet in which the temperature can be controlled. If liquid honey is required the can should be heated in the warming cabinet at about 125 °F/52 °C for perhaps 48 or 72 hours. It may then be bottled in the usual way.

It is not always necessary to liquefy honey which has granulated whilst in store because some consumers prefer it in that state, not so much the rock-hard type, but that with a 'soft-set' consistency which can be easily spread. To produce this desirable consistency, the can of hard granu-

107

lated honey should be placed in the warming cabinet at a temperature of about 90 °F/32 °C, stirring regularly to distribute the heat evenly through the mass. It may take 48 or 72 hours for the honey to reach the correct consistency. Stirring can be done with a large wooden paddle but a purpose-designed implement is available, sometimes called a 'honey creamer', which works very well. It is designed like a plunger and all that is required is to push it down into the can of honey a few times when all lumps will be dispersed. The honey is then transferred to the bottling tank and left in a warm place for about 24 hours to allow air bubbles to rise to the surface. After that it can be put into warm jars, lids firmly applied, and allowed to cool slowly. In a short time the honey will set but should not become rock hard again.

Comb honey should be packaged and marketed as soon as convenient after removal from the hive so that it reaches the consumer whilst fresh and the contained honey has not had time to start granulating. The wood or plastic of the sections should be scraped clean before they are offered for sale in cardboard cartons specially designed for the purpose. The latter are available from beekeeping appliance suppliers. Cut-comb is usually offered for sale in portions weighing about 8 oz. (227 g) Comb cutters are available which make it easy to produce portions of a regular size to fit into the available plastic containers.

An attractive special way of packing comb honey is described as 'chunk honey'. In this a piece of cut comb, as large as possible, is placed in a standard 1 lb. (454 g) jar which is then filled with liquid honey which has been heated to 150 °F and allowed to cool. This heat treatment will delay granulation. The honey used to fill the jar should be of the same colour and flavour as that in the contained comb.

Labelling

Properly prepared fresh honey is a high quality delicacy and as such deserves a high standard of presentation to the consumer. A good quality, attractive label of distinctive design greatly enhances the appearance of the product, providing it is clean and properly applied to the jar. Excellent labels, which can be over-printed with the name and address of the producer, can be obtained at reasonable cost from bee appliance suppliers.

If it is intended to sell honey for human consumption there are a number of legal requirements which must be satisfied relating to the product and to its labelling. The following is a brief summary of the regulations at the time of writing. If a beekeeper has any doubts about them he should consult his local Food Standards Officer.

The Food Safety Act (1990) makes it an offence for any person selling food for human consumption to:

"*sell to the purchaser's prejudice any food which is not of the nature, substance or quality demanded by the purchaser*"

"*give with, or displays with any food offered for sale, a label, whether or not attached to or printed on the wrapper or container, which falsely describes the food, or is likely to mislead as to the nature, substance or quality of the food*"

"*make, or be party to, any advertisement which falsely describes any food, or is likely to mislead as to the nature, substance or quality of any food*"

Bearing in mind the above Act and other existing regulations, the essential requirements of an acceptable honey jar label are as follows

1. The description of the contents should be clear and honest. For example, simple unambiguous words such as 'Honey', or 'Chunk Honey', where appropriate, cannot reasonably be misunderstood. If so desired, it is permissible to add a regional reference such as 'Norfolk Honey', 'English Honey' etc. The floral origin may be indicated such as 'Heather Honey', 'Clover Honey' etc.. Further more, the regional reference and the floral origin can be combined as, for example 'Scottish Heather Honey', providing always that the statement is accurate.

Cut comb packaged for sale

2. If the label incorporates a picture or illustration it should not mislead the consumer. For example, it would be illegal for a jar of oilseed rape honey to carry a picture of an apple orchard.

3. The label must show clearly the name and address of the producer, or the packer, or seller.

4. The nett weight must be clearly visible. For 8 oz. (227 g) and 1 lb. (454 g) jars it must be shown in print size not less than 4 millimetres. Furthermore, both the imperial and metric weights must be indicated, the figures in close proximity but distinct with the imperial weight being shown first. The only permitted units of weight and their abbreviations are pound (lb.), ounce (oz.), kilogramme (kg), and gramme (g).

5. All the required markings on a label should be clear, legible, conspicuous and indelible.

6. Although the description 'natural' is acceptable for unprocessed honey the term 'organic' should be avoided.

Apart from the above considerations relating to honey marketing, it must be recognized that standards of honey quality have been agreed throughout the European Economic Community with which, U.K. beekeepers who sell honey are obliged to comply.

Briefly, in the composition of honey the following are stipulated.

1. There should be no addition of substances to honey.

2. Honey should as far as practicable be free from mould, insects, insect debris, brood, and any other organic or inorganic substance foreign to the composition of honey. Honey with any of these defects should not be used as an ingredient of any other food.

3. The acidity should not be artificially changed. The legal maximum level of acid is not more than 40 milliequivalents per kg.

4. Any honeydew honey or blend of honeydew honey with blossom honey should have an apparent reducing sugar (invert sugar) content of not less than 60% and an apparent sucrose content of not more than 10%. Other honeys should have an apparent reducing sugar content of not less than 65% and an apparent sucrose content of not more than 5%.

5. Heather or clover honey should have a water content not exceeding 23%. Other honey must have a moisture content not exceeding 21%

6. The maximum water insoluble solids content is: Pressed honey 0.5%, Other honey 0.1%. The maximum ash content is: Honeydew honey and blends containing honeydew honey 1%, Other honey 0.6%.

7. Honey should not be heated to such extent that its natural enzymes have been destroyed or made inactive. The Diastase activity should be greater than 8, or, if it has a naturally low enzyme content, not less than 3.

8. Honey should have an hydroxymethylfurfural (HMF) content less than 40 mg/kg.

Perhaps a brief explanation of diastase and HMF content of honey might be helpful. Diastase is a natural enzyme which comes from the hypopharyngeal glands of the bee and is found in raw honey. The enzyme is rapidly destroyed by heat. Therefore, if the enzyme is absent from a sample of honey, or lower than an agreed level, it is concluded that the honey has been over-heated.

HMF is formed from the breakdown of fructose in the presence of acid. Honey contains both these components and, therefore, HMF is produced in honey to some degree all the time. The amount produced is dependent on time and also temperature. A honey which is years old will have a higher HMF content that a sample from a new crop, other factors being equal. In addition, honey when it is heated will generate HMF more quickly. The level of HMF is, therefore, taken as an indicator of the freshness of honey and, or, the degree of heat to which it has been exposed.

It should be noted that the figures quoted above for diastase activity and HMF content are those agreed by the E.E.C. members. At the time of writing the U.K. is permitted to market honey with a diastase activity of 4 units and HMF content of 80 mg/kg. No doubt we will soon harmonize quality standards at the more stringent levels set by our European partners.

Liquid and Set Honey correctly labelled

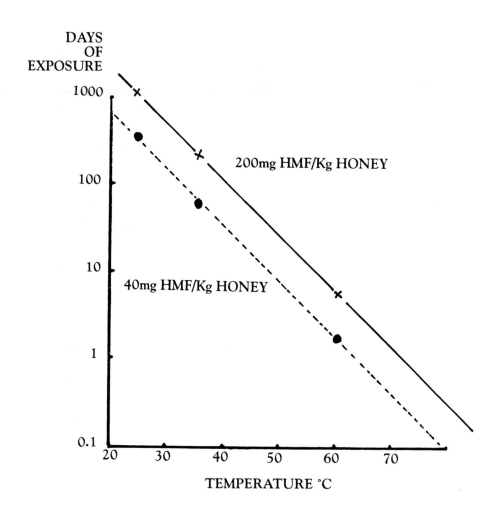

Number of days at different temperatures required to develop HMF in honey at 40 and 200 mg/kg (Reproduced from 'Bee World' by permission of the author, J.W. White)

CHAPTER 12

WAX AND PROPOLIS

Beeswax is secreted by four pairs of special wax glands which are situated on the underside of the abdomen of worker bees. The glands are most active in young bees when between the age of 12 and 18 days old, especially when food is plentiful and fresh comb is required to accommodate incoming nectar, or when a swarm is building comb for its new home.

Chemically, beeswax is a most complicated compound; one estimate is that it has more than three hundred different constituents! In simple terms it can be described as a mixture of about 70% esters (mostly myricil palmitate), 15% cerotic acid, 12% hydrocarbons, with traces of water, higher alcohols, minerals, dyes etc. It has an ill-defined melting point between 143 °F and 147 °F (62 - 64 °C) and a specific gravity of about 0.965. It is a remarkably durable substance, as exemplified by the fact that pieces recovered from ancient Egyptian tombs have remained pliable.

Bees use wax for the sole purpose of making comb, whereas man has found many uses. From the earliest times the best candles were made from beeswax and in more modern times it has been used in polishes, cosmetics, waterproofing, insulation in the electrical industry, industrial mouldings and in dentistry. It is a valuable product in that it commands a good price, but more importantly, it should be carefully husbanded by the beekeeper because it is not produced cheaply by his bees. It has been estimated that bees may consume six or seven pounds of honey in making one pound of wax.

The main source of wax for the beekeeper is from cappings and pieces of broken comb etc. at extracting time. Old brood combs do, of course, contain wax but it requires quite a lot of effort to get it out of them. It should, however, be possible to recover between one and two pounds from a box of ten old standard brood combs.

The most convenient method of salvaging wax from cappings and old combs is by means of a solar wax extractor. This is basically a well insulated box with a double glazed lid. When placed in direct sunlight in the summer months, the temperature inside will rise above the melting point of wax. If the cappings, or combs, are placed on a sloping tray inside the box, the molten wax will run down and can be directed into a collecting receptacle. Solar extractors have the great attraction that there are no fuel costs and they do improve the wax by bleaching it a little. Furthermore, they have the great convenience that odds and ends of wax can be put into them at any time as they come to hand during the season. It is true that old combs will not give up all their wax in a solar extractor but, in practice, the ease and convenience of the method makes this slight loss acceptable.

Special wax extracting appliances, using steam or hot water, are available from beekeeping appliance suppliers. However, a cheap arrangement is to use a large clean tin which will fit into a large saucepan. The tin is one-third filled with clean rainwater and stood on some pebbles which have been placed in the bottom of the saucepan. The saucepan is then ³/₄ filled with ordinary tap water and brought to the boil and kept simmering. Clean pieces of wax, or cappings are added to the tin. The hot rainwater will melt the wax which will rise to the surface, whilst most of the debris will remain in the water. When the tin is removed from the saucepan and allowed to cool, the wax will solidify as a cake and can be removed. It must be emphasized that only rainwater, or distilled water, should be used in the tin because wax deteriorates if boiled in hard water. When the cake of wax is removed from the tin there will be a certain amount of debris stuck to the undersurface which should be cut away. Clean cakes of pure beeswax will be accepted by beekeeping appliance suppliers in part exchange for new comb foundation, or other equipment.

The above method is suitable for use with cappings or pieces of clean broken comb from which there is likely to be a good return of wax. When dealing with quantities of old brood combs the process needs to be on a larger scale, although the basic principle remains the same. A large metal oil drum should be well cleaned and a couple of inches of small clean pebbles placed in the bottom. It can then be stood on bricks, leaving space for a gas ring burner underneath and half filled with clean rainwater. The old combs should be well broken and enclosed in a sack with enough pebbles to make it sink. This is placed in the drum and allowed to soak for 24 hours. After that the burner is lit and the rainwater brought to the boil and allowed to simmer. Wax will float to the surface and more can be obtained if the sack is prodded from time to time with a wood plunger. After completion of this extraction process the drum is allowed to cool, when the cake of solidified wax on the surface can be removed.

Exhibits of beeswax are a feature of honey shows. To make a prize winning cake of wax requires meticulous care and great patience. The best wax for exhibition purposes comes from cappings because it is of good quality and usually of an attractive light colour. After washing the cappings in cold rainwater, they should be dried and any dark pieces and propolis etc. should be removed. Drying can be conveniently carried out in a greenhouse, or conservatory, with the cappings spread on a piece of white sheet. When dry, and all dark pieces removed, the wax can be recovered in a solar extractor, or by a hot water or steam method. The wax that is obtained should then be broken into small pieces and re-melted carefully in a pyrex jug standing in a saucepan of boiling water. When the wax is fully liquefied and at a temperature of about 170 °F (77 °C) it should be filtered through flannel, or white surgical lint with fluffy side up, re-melted again and finally passed through filter paper. It is then ready for casting in a suitable mould. Pyrex glass bowls make suitable moulds, providing there are no defects in the glass. The mould should be washed carefully in hot water containing detergent and dried with a non-fluffy cloth. Add two or three drops of distilled water to the mould with a couple of drops of 'Liquid Fairy' and rub this around the inside of the mould with a clean finger until the surface appears dry. While preparing the mould the wax should be melting in a pyrex jug standing in a saucepan of simmering water, making sure that the temperature of the liquid wax does not rise above 194 °F (90 °C). The mould should be kept warm in an oven, together with a small piece of plate glass which will be used for its lid. When it comes to pouring, the mould is placed in a washing up bowl containing hot water at 151 °F (66 °C) making sure that none of this water gets into the mould. The wax, at a temperature of 158 °F (70 °C), is then poured into the mould and covered with the piece of hot plate glass. More hot water is added to the washing up bowl to bring the water level up to that of the surface of the wax in the mould. Cover everything with warm towels and leave severely alone for several hours. It is convenient to cast wax in this way last thing at night so that it can be left until the following morning without disturbance. When the wax has cooled and solidified it can be released from the mould by immersing it in a bucket of cold water, which should cause the wax to float out. It can then be given a light polish with a soft silk handkerchief. Described in this way, it may all sound simple and straightforward, but disappointments are frequent and the would-be wax exhibitor must be prepared to repeat the process until success is achieved.

The following expression of opinion will probably be considered a heresy by wax exhibitors and no doubt the author will be remorselessly pilloried! Nevertheless, with full awareness that fools rush in where angels fear to tread, I suggest, with great respect, that devoting hours and hours to the preparation of a cake of show wax, which has no inherent use, is really an occupation for those with time to spare! Much better to make wax articles which are both beautiful and useful. I refer,

Pure beeswax candles

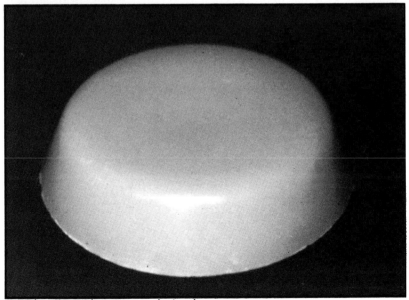

A cake of pure beeswax made for showing

of course, to pure beeswax candles which, when well made, are items of great charm, burning brightly with a smokeless flame and are long-lasting! Furthermore, those who make beeswax candles have the immense satisfaction of knowing that they are continuing an ancient and honourable craft going back to pre-Christian times. Recognizable candles still survive from the first century A.D.!

Beeswax candles can be made by pouring, dipping and moulding. An excellent guide to these various methods has been written by Clara Furness and is available from British Bee Publications Ltd.

Propolis, or bee glue, is the name of the resinous substance collected by bees from various plant sources. It appears that much of it comes from sticky buds found on horse-chestnut, poplar, birch, elm, alder and conifers etc. In the hive, propolis varies from light yellow to dark brown. It has an aromatic odour and although soft at summer temperatures, it becomes brittle when cold. Chemically it is a most complicated substance with many constituents not yet identified. It is insoluble in water, soluble in ether and chloroform, partly soluble in alcohol, and very slightly soluble in turpentine.

Bees use propolis to seal and waterproof their hives. They also use it to anchor parts together, to seal holes and cracks, repair combs, strengthen the thin borders of combs, and to reduce the size of the hive entrance so that it is easier to defend. Propolis is also used to embalm dead hive invaders such as mice which are too big for the bees to remove. It can be a nuisance for the beekeeper if it is used to excess and some breeders therefore try to select strains which use it sparingly. Caucasian bees have a reputation for using it extravagantly.

Medicinal qualities have been attributed to propolis in folk medicine for a very long time. In the last hundred years or so it has been used in conventional medicine, it being documented that it was used successfully in the Boer war as an application for the treatment of wounds. In more recent years it has been shown to possess anti-bacterial and anti-fungal properties and that it also acts as a local anaesthetic. At the present time its medicinal use seems to be much greater on the Continent than in the British Isles, but there is an increasing interest in the substance. From time to time advertisements appear in the bee journals offering to purchase propolis from beekeepers. Good prices are paid for top grade material.

CHAPTER 13

DISEASES

The honeybee suffers from a number of diseases but with good apiary management these can be kept to a minimum. As prevention is always better than cure, it must never be forgotten that disease can be introduced into an apiary by contaminated second-hand equipment and by collecting stray swarms of unknown origin. A wise precaution, therefore, is to carefully clean and sterilize all used equipment immediately after purchase and to isolate stray swarms until it is confirmed that they are healthy. Because unhealthy bees are likely to soil their combs when confined for long periods by inclement winter weather, another precautionary action which will help minimize disease is to renew brood combs regularly, perhaps every two or three years.

DISEASES OF ADULT BEES

Acarine

The respiratory system of the adult bee consists of numerous breathing tubes (tracheae) and air sacs. These carry air to all parts of the insect body from openings (spiracles) situated along the side of the thorax and abdomen. Acarine disease is an infestation of adult bees by a parasitic mite, Acarapis woodi Rennie, which invades and breeds in the tracheae of the thorax leading from the first pair of spiracles. The mites multiply and spread from bee to bee, but it appears that only young bees under five days old are susceptible. Infestation usually reaches a maximum in spring and autumn when young bees are present and clustering occurs in colder spells of weather. The disease is not usually a problem in the summer months. Bees infested with the mite have a shorter life span

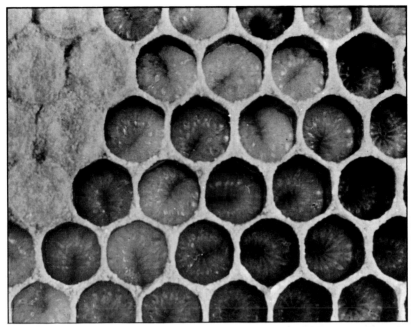

Healthy brood (from Bulletin 100 - HMSO - 'Diseases of Bees' - Crown Copyright)

than healthy bees, the result is that colonies tend to dwindle in size, especially in spring. If a colony is heavily infested in autumn it is very likely to die out during the winter. Outwardly, there may be few signs that a colony is infested, apart from dwindling in strength. On other occasions there may be numerous bees crawling outside the front of the hive and unable to fly. Sometimes their wings are held in an abnormal position, giving the appearance that they are dislocated, the so-called 'K wing'.

The disease is accurately diagnosed by dissection to expose the tracheae for examination under a low power microscope. The normal tracheae are creamy white, whilst those that are infested will appear dark and discoloured. The actual mites can usually be seen.

Available treatment is very limited at the present time. That usually recommended is fumigation with smoke emitted by burning Folbex VA, a proprietary product marketed by Ciba-Geigy, but which has recently been withdrawn. It is anticipated that new aracacide treatments will be introduced in the future but at the time of writing none are available. In North America fumigation with menthol crystals is popular but the effectiveness is not really clear.

Nosema

This is a relatively common disease. It is caused by a microscopic spore-forming protozoan organism, Nosema Apis, which invades the lining cells of the mid-gut of the adult bee. When inside these cells the organisms grow and multiply at the expense of the host cells, which are eventually destroyed. Before the cells die and rupture, the nosema organism forms numerous spores which are liberated into the gut. From there they are carried to the outside in excreta. If these spores are ingested by another bee, the whole cycle is repeated. The effect of this infection on the individual bee is to shorten its life. When many bees in a colony are infected the result is a dwindling of the colony and sometimes complete loss. Very often the infected bees show no outward signs of disease but sometimes the infection is associated with dysentery. At other times bees may be so weakened that they are unable to fly. Contaminated brood combs can be carriers of the infection from year to year. Confirmation of the disease requires microscopic examination of the abdominal contents of bees to establish the presence of nosema spores. The technique is quite easy for the amateur to master, providing he has access to a microscope.

Treatment

If a colony is found to have nosema in the spring, the best treatment is to get that colony onto a new set of combs. In early May make up a brood box with frames containing foundation. Find the queen in the infected colony and remove the frame with her on it and place it in the centre of the new box of foundation, marking the frame with a drawing pin in the top bar. Place a queen excluder on the old brood box and above this position the new box containing the queen. Finally, add a cover board with a feeder over the feed hole. Whilst drawing comb in the new brood box the bees will require feeding with liberal quantities of sugar syrup to which has been added the antibiotic 'Fumidil B'. This is active against the vegetative stage of nosema, but not the spores, and can be obtained from Bee Diseases Insurance Ltd. Instructions on use are normally supplied with the antibiotic but, in brief, it comes in a three dose pack. One dose is mixed into 1 $1/2$ gallons of strong cold sugar syrup and fed to the bees until it has all been taken.

At the end of a week, much of the foundation will have been drawn into comb and the queen will have moved off her old comb onto one of the new ones. Ascertain that this is so, and then remove the old comb, placing it back in the bottom brood box below the excluder. After about three weeks, all brood will have emerged from the combs in the bottom brood box which should then be removed. If the combs in this box are black with old age, distorted, and with many drone cells, they should be discarded. If, however, they are in good condition they can be used again after sterilization.

Combs contaminated with nosema can be effectively sterilized with the fumes from 80% acetic acid as follows. First remove the frames from the brood box and clean its inside by scraping away any pieces of wax or propolis. The inside should then be flamed with a blow lamp. If the box has metal frame-supporting runners these should be lightly covered with vaseline to protect them against corrosion by the acetic acid. The box should then be placed on a flat piece of wood, or hardboard, in a sheltered outdoor spot and the frames replaced, after removing any metal ends. On the top of the frames place a saucer containing a pad of cotton wool onto which is poured $1/4$ pint (142 ml) of acetic acid. This is prepared by diluting four parts by volume of Glacial acetic acid with one part by volume of water. Always measure out the water first and then slowly add the measured quantity of acetic acid to the water - not the other way around!

When the acetic acid has been placed in the saucer an empty super box is applied, together with a lid, and the whole assembly made as air tight as possible and left for a week. After this fumigation, the combs should be aired for 48 hours and can then be safely used again.

Some beekeepers add Fumidil B to the autumn feed as a regular prophylactic remedy against nosema. This is not the practice of the author who believes that with good apiary management, which includes regular replacement of old brood combs, the disease should not be a problem. Fumidil B is reserved for those rare occasions when there is a failure of good husbandry methods.

Amoeba

The cyst-forming, protozoan organism, Malpighamoeba mellificae Prell, invades and damages the Malpighian tubules (excretory organs) of the bee. The organism develops at the expense of the lining cells of the excretory tubules and forms cysts which are passed out in excreta. The effect on a colony is uncertain but most authorities consider it to be harmful. There are no obvious symptoms caused by the infection and no specific treatment. Good brood comb hygiene, as advocated for the control of nosema, is a worthwhile preventative measure.

Paralysis

Dr. Leslie Bailey did extensive research at Rothamsted on virus infections which cause paralysis of honeybees and readers who require detailed information are referred to Dr. Bailey's publications.

In the U.K. the main problem is Chronic Paralysis, which occurs in two forms, or types. The commonest of these is described as Type 1 and manifests itself as a trembling motion of the wings and bodies of the affected bees. The bees seem unable to fly and crawl in large numbers from the hive, climbing up grass stems etc. They often have bloated abdomens and usually die in a few days.

The other form which is encountered is Type 2. In this the bees appear small, hairless, and dark in colour. They have often been described by beekeepers as 'little blacks'. In a few days they also show trembling and inability to fly and eventually die. Both type 1 and 2 can occur in the same colony. Chronic paralysis is caused by a virus infection for which there is no specific treatment. Many beekeepers believe that re-queening from a different strain is beneficial.

Dysentery

In beekeeping usage this is the name given to the condition in which bees foul their combs and the inside of the hive with excrement. It is not an infectious disease and is often due to unsuitable dietary items in winter such as fermented, or coarsely granulated stores. It is sometimes associated with nosema infection.

Poisoning

Clearly, this is not a disease of bees, but is something which has to be considered when a colony is showing an excessive number of dead and dying bees around the hive in spring and early summer. Insecticide sprays are used extensively in horticulture and agriculture for the control of crop pests. Unfortunately, they are equally as toxic to the honeybee as to the pests that they are intended to eliminate. Bees are most likely to be affected if spraying is done when a crop is in full blossom. In the instructions given to sprayers, the manufacturers make it quite clear that spraying should not be undertaken when blossom is fully open because of the danger to bees and other beneficial insects. Sadly, however, there are always a few incidents each year when, through ignorance or selfish disregard of environmental responsibilities, these instructions are ignored. In those areas where the beekeeper is aware of crops that are likely to be sprayed (e.g. oilseed rape, orchards, soft fruit etc.), it is a helpful measure to get to know the farmer, or horticulturist, to explain that you have bees in the vicinity and that they will be at risk if he sprays at an inappropriate time. Most farmers are very co-operative in these matters.

The diagnosis of poisoning can be confirmed by specialist chemical analysis of dead bees. For this purpose a sample of at least 200 dead or dying bees is required. This is approximately equivalent to four matchboxes full of bees. The bees should be as fresh as possible and not in an advanced state of decomposition. The sample can be despatched by post in a small cardboard container. Sealed plastic bags, or tins, should not be used as they tend to accelerate decomposition. The sample should be sent to the National Beekeeping Specialist, at the National Beekeeping Unit, Luddington, Stratford-upon-Avon, CV37 9SJ together with a full written statement about all the known circumstances. The B.B.K.A. Spray & Pesticides Committee publishes a most helpful leaflet which gives clear instructions on the steps to be taken when insecticide poisoning of honeybees is suspected. The leaflet can be obtained from the B.B.K.A. office at Stoneleigh.

Brood Diseases

The term 'Foul Brood' relates to two bacterial diseases of honeybee larvae; one is called American Foul Brood (AFB), and the other European Foul Brood (EFB). Of the two, American Foul Brood is the most serious and widespread brood disease in Great Britain.

American Foul Brood (AFB)

American foul brood is caused by a spore-forming bacterium called Bacillus larvae. The spores are very resistant to heat, chemical disinfectants and desiccation. They retain their powers of germination for many years in honey, old combs and derelict hives etc.

Very young honeybee larvae become infected when they ingest B. larvae spores in their food. It appears that larvae under 24 hours old are especially susceptible whereas those more than two days old are much more resistant. When ingested by a very young larva the spores germinate rapidly in the gut into the vegetative form of B. larvae. The latter multiply quickly feeding on the tissues of the larva, eventually causing its death in the propupal stage, which is about eleven days after hatching. This is soon after the larva has been sealed in its cell. When

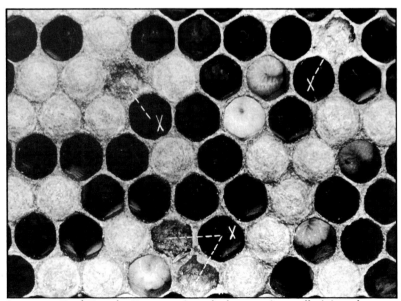

American Foul Brood - Portion of comb showing four cells (x) with cappings becoming dark and sunken (From Bulletin 100 - HMSO - 'Diseases of Bees' - Crown Copyright)

an infected larva dies the bacteria no longer have a food supply so they revert back to the spore stage. The remains of a larva can contain many millions of spores which are subsequently liberated and disseminated in the colony with fatal results.

American foul brood can be diagnosed by visual inspection of brood combs. Infected larvae die within the sealed cell causing changes in the appearance of the cell cappings. The latter become discoloured, sunken and some may have perforations. If a matchstick is inserted through a discoloured capping into an infected cell and withdrawn slowly, the contents will come out as a brown mucus-like thread or 'rope'. After this ropiness stage the larval remains gradually dry to be finally left as a dark brown scale lying on the lower side of the cell. These scales adhere tightly and can only be removed by the bees with great difficulty. They therefore persist for years in the combs of colonies which have died from the disease.

There is no effective curative treatment for the disease and infected colonies and combs etc. should be destroyed by fire. In England and Wales the Ministry of Agriculture trains and appoints Bee Disease Officers who have the right to inspect all bee colonies. If AFB is discovered they can order the destruction of the infected colonies.

The Bee Diseases Control Order 1982 empowers the appropriate Agriculture Departments of Great Britain to take measures to control American Foul Brood and European Foul Brood.

Any beekeeper who suspects the presence of foul brood in a colony is required to contact the local office of the relevant Agriculture department and is obliged to have the colony officially examined, or must submit combs for examination.

Best angle of view to see dried scales of American Foul Brood (From Bulletin 100 - HMSO - 'Diseases of Bees' - Crown Copyright)

European Foul Brood (EFB)

European foul brood is a disease of honeybee larvae caused by the bacterium Melissococcus pluton. The infecting bacteria are transmitted to the larvae in food and multiply in the cavity of the mid-gut. Larvae which die from the disease do so when they are about four days old, which is before their cells are sealed.

Healthy larvae are pearly white, each lying head to tail in a circular flat position on the bottom of a cell. In contrast, diseased larvae are found in contorted unnatural positions and when they die become discoloured, turn yellowish-brown, and eventually collapse to form a loosely attached brown scale. In a major outbreak the decomposing larvae give the brood chamber a foul sour smell. The disease may spread rapidly

131

through a colony so that it dies, but more often it runs a prolonged course in which it waxes and wanes. The disease cannot be diagnosed with absolute certainty by visual inspection alone because it can be confused with other disorders. Confirmation of the diagnosis is achieved by bacteriological isolation of M. pluton from larval gut contents.

Colonies with a high proportion of diseased brood should be destroyed by fire, as with American foul brood. However, the disease will respond to antibiotics and some lightly affected colonies, at the discretion of the Bee Disease Officer and with the agreement of the owner, may be treated. The antibiotic normally used is 'Terramycin' (oxy-tetracycline) in the dose range of 0.5 to 1 g per colony, fed in sugar syrup. Treatment must be carried out only by an Appointed Officer under the Bee Diseases Control Order 1982, using drugs officially dispensed following confirmation of EFB in sample combs submitted for diagnosis to an approved laboratory.

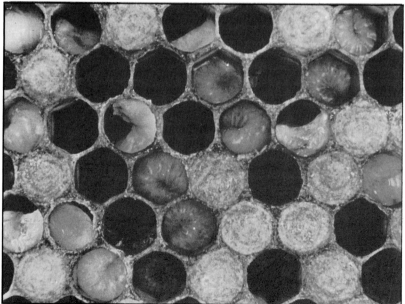

European Foul Brood - Note unsealed larvae in various stages of collapse (From Bulletin 100 - HMSO - 'Diseases of Bees' - Crown Copyright)

Examinations of bees and combs for foul brood is a statutory responsibility of the ADAS National Beekeeping Unit at Luddington and is undertaken without charge.

Bee Disease Insurance Ltd. is a non-profit making organization founded more than fifty years ago with the object of providing compensation to beekeepers who had their bees destroyed under Ministry orders because of foul brood. Local beekeeper associations pay premiums to the company so that their membership is covered for the benefit of this insurance.

Chalk Brood

This disorder takes its name from the chalky-white appearance of the dead brood. It is caused by the fungus Ascophaera apis. The fungus spores reach the larvae in their food and subsequently germinate to create a mycelium in the lumen of the gut. Larvae usually die about two days after the cells are sealed. It appears that larvae which have been chilled are more susceptible to infection. For that reason the beekeeper should endeavour not to expose brood combs unnecessarily when inspecting colonies in poor weather.

After they have died the larvae shrink and become hard and loose in the cells. The bees will uncap many of the cells making the contents visible to the beekeeper. Furthermore, the bees will remove many of these 'mummies' and deposit them on the alighting board at the front of the hive, which should draw the attention of the beekeeper to the problem. There is no specific treatment available. Infected combs can, however, be sterilized by fumigation with acetic acid as previously described for nosema. The disease is common but does not usually threaten the survival of colonies. It has been described as a nuisance rather than a disaster by Professor Len Heath who has made a special study of the disorder.

Some beekeepers believe it is helpful as a possible control measure to re-queen a heavily infected colony with a queen from a different strain. The rationale of this, presumably, is that there is a genetic variation in the susceptibility of different strains of honeybees to the disease.

Sac Brood

This is a virus disorder which is fairly common and, like chalk brood, can reasonably be described as a nuisance rather than a disaster. Infected larvae die after sealing in their cells. They fail to pupate and fluid accumulates between the body of the diseased larvae and their tough unshed skins. The body colour of the larvae change from pearly-white to yellow and after it has died it becomes dark brown. The head and thorax darken first making a rather distinctive appearance which helps diagnosis. Finally, the larvae dry down to flattened gondola-shaped scales. There is no specific treatment but it is worth re-queening colonies in which the disorder persists.

Varroassis

Varroasis is the parasitisation of larval and adult honeybees by the mite Varroa jacobsoni. Fortunately, up to the time of writing it has not been identified in the British Isles, although it is present all over continental Europe, and much of the rest of the world. It seems appropriate to give a brief description here so that beekeepers can be alert to the threat that this mite poses should it arrive in these islands.

The mite was first described by Oudemans in 1904 who recognized it in the brood cells of Apis cerana, the Eastern honeybee. It appears that the mite lives with some degree of compatibility with Apis cerana, its traditional host, and the survival of infested colonies of that bee is not jeopardized. Sadly, when beekeepers introduced colonies of Apis mellifera into the Far East, the mite soon spread to them with devastating results, in that heavily infested colonies invariably succumbed. Unfortunately, through the activities of migratory beekeepers and bee breeders, the mite was transported from the Far East to Western Europe where it quickly spread so that today, it is little more than 20 miles from the shores of Kent.

Within an apiary, mites are spread from infested colonies on drifting worker and drone bees. They can also be carried longer distances on swarms. Mites on adult bees are usually found on the underside of the abdomen between the sclerites and for that reason may be difficult to spot. They feed on the haemolymph of the bee by piercing the soft tissue between the abdominal sclerites. This in itself is damaging enough but, in addition, it further jeopardizes the health of the bee by creating a portal of entry for bacterial and viral infections.

Once inside a colony with brood, varroa becomes mainly a parasite of larvae. The adult female mite is about 1.1 mm long and 1.6 mm wide, redish brown in colour, large enough to be seen with the naked eye. She starts the reproductive cycle by entering an uncapped cell containing a larva about 5 days old, preferring drone larvae. She consumes what larval food is available and when this is exhausted will begin to feed on the haemolymph of the larva. When the cell is capped eggs will be laid from which will develop larval mites which also feed on the bee larva. The mite takes 5 to 7 days to develop from egg to adult. Although the majority of bee larvae survive and develop into adult bees many are deformed, especially if the mite infestation is heavy.

One of the major problems of varroa infestation is the difficulty of early detection. When there are only a few mites in a large colony detection is just about impossible, and when infestation is heavy, and is spotted by the beekeeper, it probably means that the mites have been present a couple of years, or more! Two methods for early detection have been advised in the U.K.. One is to insert a piece of stiff paper to cover the floor of the hive in autumn and to retrieve this paper insert in the spring and examine the debris for mites which may have fallen from the bees during the winter. The National Beekeeping Unit at Luddington has arranged an examination service for the debris from such inserts.

The alternative advised method involves fumigation with tobacco smoke which is toxic to the mites. The method of use is quite critical and the reader is therefore referred to M.A.F.F. Leaflets 936 and P834 for precise guidance.

At the time of writing there is no approved treatment available in the U.K. for varroasis but a number of acaracides are being used experimentally and it is anticipated that treatment will be made available here if the disease arrives.

At this juncture it is appropriate to mention Braula coeca, the bee louse, which to the inexperienced eye might possibly be confused with Varroa jacobsoni. Braula coeca is a wingless fly, about $^1/_{16}$ inch (1.5 mm) long, which is often found on bees. Although it can be an irritation to the infested bee it does it no direct harm. It gains its nourishment by gleaning food remnants that it finds around the mouth parts of the bee. Queen bees are often badly infested with them, sometimes dozens are found on one queen. Some beekeepers claim that a queen can be de-loused quickly by blowing cigarette smoke over her. Unfortunately, Braula lay their eggs on cappings over honey. The young burrow under the cappings and disfigure them which is undesirable in comb honey for exhibition or sale.

CHAPTER 14

STINGS

Honeybees have no great desire to sting and will only do so in defence of themselves and their colonies. Drones do not have a sting and are, therefore, quite harmless. Queen bees have a sting and can use it on humans but only do so in rare and unusual circumstances. The real target for a queen's sting is a rival queen! The task of colony defence falls upon worker bees when they are about 18 or 19 days old, just before they start their foraging activities.

The sting is hidden inside a cavity, the sting chamber, at the tip of the abdomen, from where it can be quickly protruded. The precise anatomy of the sting will not be detailed here and for present purposes it can be regarded as a tapering, barbed tube, which can be thrust into an enemy and through which venom is injected. When a bee thrusts her sting into the elastic skin of a human she is unable to withdraw it because of its barbs. In her struggle to do so, the sting and associated structures, are torn from the bee's abdomen and is a mortal injury. It is interesting to note that bees can withdraw their stings when fighting other bees and similar insects with rigid exoskeletons.

Bee venom is a complicated mixture of toxic proteins and enzymes. When injected into the human skin by a stinging bee they cause pain and swelling. The site of the sting will be seen immediately as a red spot, with the sting embedded. In a minute or two this will develop into a white raised weal which will be surrounded later by a red inflamed area. The first time a person is stung it will be painful, but there may not be much swelling. With subsequent stings more swelling is likely to ensue but in the course of time, with further stings, it will be noted that they provoke less and less reaction until eventually the response is minimal.

The time it takes to develop this relative immunity varies greatly between individuals. Some achieve it quickly, others slowly, and unfortunately a tiny minority may never reach that happy state.

Local reactions of pain and swelling at the site of a sting are unpleasant, but of no serious consequence when confined to the arms, legs, or trunk, but can be dangerous in certain other parts, such as the eyes, mouth and throat. For this reason a properly fitting veil should always be worn when manipulating bees.

Unfortunately, a very small number of people suffer a general reaction when stung. Some develop an itchy nettle rash all over the body, others feel wheezy in the chest, some feel ill and nauseated, whilst in more extreme circumstances some may collapse and faint. The cause of these unpleasant symptoms is the development of an allergic (hypersensitive) intolerance of the proteins in bee venom. Although serious general reactions are not common, anyone suffering from other allergic disorders such as hay-fever, asthma, eczema, etc., should exercise caution as they are a little more likely to react badly to stings. Clearly, anyone who suffers a general reaction after a sting should consult a doctor for advice.

The immediate treatment of a sting is to remove the bee's sting apparatus which will be seen embedded in the skin. This is best done by scraping it out with a finger-nail. Do not grasp the sting directly in order to pull it out as this will only squeeze more venom into the wound.

All sorts of anecdotal remedies have been advised by beekeepers as beneficial applications to relieve the pain and swelling of stings. These include honey, propolis extracts, blue bag, mallow leaves, meat tender-iser, antihistamine cream etc. etc. Normally, no local applications are required, but something simple such as an ice-pack, or calamine lotion can be used to soothe. A couple of aspirin tablets by mouth will help to lessen inflammation. If swelling is extensive, hot, and itchy, a steroid cream application such as Betnovate is helpful.

In a serious general reaction, where collapse occurs, a doctor and ambulance should be called urgently. Pending arrival of medical aid the victim should be laid flat, clothing loosened, especially around the neck, covered with a blanket to keep warm, and any dentures removed. If available, and the victim is able to swallow, an antihistamine tablet such as Piriton 4 mg, or Triludan 60 mg, should be given as soon as possible.

If a beekeeper experiences mild general reactions, such as an itchy nettle rash after being stung, it has been found that much benefit can result from taking an antihistamine tablet an hour or so before attending his bees. The rationale of this is that the medication will have been absorbed from the gut and distributed throughout the body before there is any risk of a sting. It is well known that one of the most potent substances liberated in the body in an allergic reaction, and which causes many of the alarming symptoms, is histamine. This very potent agent works very quickly after liberation and for that reason it is not much good taking an antihistamine tablet by mouth after the sting has occurred, because it will take at least half an hour for the drug to be absorbed from the gut and circulated around the body.

Some people are made drowsy by the ordinary antihistamine tablets such as Piriton (4 mg) and should not drive cars when taking this medication. Fortunately, the newer preparations such as Triludan tablets (60 mg) do not have this sedating effect and are to be preferred. They can be purchased from a chemist without prescription.

Another precaution which can be taken by a beekeeper who suffers mild general reactions, apart from taking antihistamine tablets, is to ask his doctor if he will kindly prescribe an aerosol spray inhaler of adrenaline ('Medihaler-Epi' Riker) for emergency use. The preparation should be inhaled according to instructions immediately after a sting and has much the same benefit as an injection of adrenaline, but not so potent.

Those who still suffer general allergic reactions despite these simple measures should consult their doctor because desensitizing treatment for bee venom allergy is available at some hospital allergy clinics.

Reading this chapter may cause the beginner some alarm and despondency. That is not the intention and it may help to keep the problem in perspective if it is remembered that bee stings are to a great extent ignored by beekeepers in their thousands throughout the world, since they suffer so few ill-effects from them.

CHAPTER 15

MEAD

Mead is an alcoholic drink made by fermenting honey in water with yeast. For thousands of years honey was the only sweet fermentable substance generally available and it is, therefore, a very plausible conjecture that mead was the first alcoholic beverage that man imbibed. Today, a number of beekeepers derive great pleasure and satisfaction from producing mead and in so doing consider themselves privileged custodians of an art of great antiquity.

Mead can be made dry or sweet as desired. It can be flavoured with various fruit juices and spices, in which circumstances specific names are given to the different beverages. Pyment is made from honey and pure grape juice; cyser contains pure apple juice and honey; melomel is made by fermenting honey with any fruit juice, apart from grape or apple; whilst metheglin is sweet or dry mead to which spices have been added.

To make mead the only essential pieces of equipment are a one gallon demijohn, an air-lock, some plastic tubing for siphoning, and sterilized wine bottles and corks. It cannot be emphasized too strongly that in home wine making and brewing, strict hygiene and sterilization of all equipment is essential. An effective sterilizing solution can be made by dissolving one teaspoonful of sodium metabisulphite and an equal quantity of citric acid in a pint of cold water. These requisites can be obtained from any shop selling home brewing items.

A general recipe for dry mead is as follows

3 lbs of Light Honey
6 pints of water
1 teaspoon of yeast nutrient
$^1/_4$ teaspoon of grape tannin (or two tablespoons of cold strong tea)
2 level teaspoons of citric acid (or the juice of a lemon)
Chablis Wine Yeast.

Raw honey contains many wild yeasts and fungi which will grow and ferment in the honey and water mixture if allowed to do so. This should be prevented because the fermentation they cause can produce unpleasant off-flavours and aromas. The honey and water mixture (known as the 'must') should, therefore, be sterilized before an authentic wine yeast is added. There are two widely used methods; one uses heat and the other metabisulphite.

Heat Sterilization of the Must

To the water add the honey, yeast nutrient, acid and tannin and heat to 150 °F (66 °C). Allow to simmer at this temperature for only a few minutes, then skim off the froth and allow to cool. When the temperature has fallen to 70 °F (21 °C) add the selected wine yeast, pour into the demijohn, fit an air-lock, and place in a warm cupboard. In 24 hours or so, fermentation will be apparent by rising small bubbles in the must and bubbles escaping through the air-lock. When fermentation is no longer vigorous, the demijohn should be topped up with water so that there is only a small air space below the air-lock. Leave until fermentation is complete and the mead tastes quite dry. This may take three or four weeks after which the mead will begin to clear and a deposit will form in the bottom of the jar. At this time the mead should be siphoned off the deposit into a clean receptacle. After discarding the deposit the demijohn is rinsed clean and refilled with the mead. One

Campden tablet (metabisulphite) should be added at this stage and the jar topped up with water. It should be stored in a cool dark place. If, in a few weeks, further deposit forms in the bottom of the jar the mead should again be siphoned off and the deposit discarded as before. In wine-making circles this siphoning procedure is called 'racking'. It is a wise precaution to add a Campden tablet after each racking to prevent contamination with bacteria or other organisms. The mead can be bottled after about a year and should be in good condition to drink after a further year.

Sweet mead is made similarly, except that some favour the use of a Sauterne or Tokay yeast. After the first fermentation when the wine tastes dry, a further 8oz of honey is added and fermentation allowed to continue. A few weeks later the mead is tasted again and if still dry a further 4 oz. of honey is added. This procedure is repeated (called 'feeding the must') until the build up of alcohol reaches a level which suppresses the activity of the yeast. At this point there remains in the must some unfermented honey which gives the mead its sweetness. Four or five pounds of honey may be used in this process and the mead will have a high alcohol content. It will take longer to mature and will benefit by being left in bottle for three or more years. A strong sweet mead is best drunk as a social wine, perhaps ideally whilst relaxing on a cold winter evening. Many would consider it too potent for use as a table wine!

Cold Sterilization of the Must with Campden Tablets

Some wine makers believe that heating a must to sterilize destroys some of the contained aromatic substances. For that reason they prefer a cold sterilizing method such as the following. Place six pints of water in the demijohn, together with the honey, yeast nutrient, and tannin. Add one Campden tablet, fit an air-lock and leave the jar in a warm place for about 24 hours. During that time sulphur dioxide released from the

Campden tablet will kill any wild yeasts and fungi. Because the presence of sulphur dioxide inhibits all yeasts to some extent, it is desirable to add the selected wine yeast to the must in a vigorously active state. This is easily achieved by starting the wine yeast into active growth by placing it in a small bottle with 5 oz. of water to which has been added a teaspoonful of sugar, a pinch of yeast nutrient and a little lemon juice. This should be kept warm for 24 hours by which time the yeast will be fully active and ready to add to the must. With this method fermentation is often a little slow initially but should be visible after a day or two. The further stages of the procedure are identical with those described previously in the heat treatment method.

Mead deserves to be served properly; good presentation adds to the enjoyment of a quality product! (The House of Lords wine goblet (left) was a special award for mead won by the author at the 1981 Golden Jubilee National Honey Show)

Additives used in Mead Making

A brief explanation of the function of the additives included in the above recipes for mead might help those without experience in home wine making.

Acids play an important part in fermentation. Wine yeasts grow best in an acid medium and without adequate acid unpleasant off-flavours may be produced. Although honey is slightly acid it does not contain sufficient for a good reliable fermentation.

Yeast nutrients are simple salts containing nitrogen, such as ammonium phosphate, which are essential for the growth of yeast. Honey is deficient as a source of nitrogen.

Tannin gives a degree of astringency to the final product. Without it mead would taste insipid and bland.

Examples of other Recipes

Pyment

6 pints of pure grape juice, 2 lbs light honey, water to 1 gallon, Chablis yeast.

Method. Place juice, 1 lb. of honey and yeast in demijohn, fit air lock, and put in warm cupboard. About a week later, when the initial vigorous fermentation has settled, add the remaining 1 lb. of honey and top up jar with water. Subsequent procedure is as described earlier for dry mead.

Cyser

> 6 pints pure apple juice, 2½ lbs light honey, water to 1 gallon, Bordeaux yeast.

Method. As described above for Pyment, except 1½ lbs honey can be put into the demijohn initially.

Gooseberry Melomel (Dry)

> 3 lbs green gooseberries, 3 lbs light honey, teaspoon yeast nutrient, pinch of grape tannin, water to 1 gallon, Chablis yeast.

Method. Crush, or coarsely pulp the gooseberries in a food processor. Place in a plastic fermentation bucket and cover with 6 pints of water. Add 1 Campden tablet, cover the receptacle with a cloth and keep in the warm. After 24 hours dissolve the honey in 2 pints of warm water and add to the must with the yeast nutrient, tannin and the wine yeast. Ferment on the pulp for three days, stirring each day. After that strain into the demijohn, fit an air lock and ferment until dry. Subsequent care as for dry mead.

APPENDIX 1

CONVERSION TABLES

Weight.

1 Kilogramme = 2.2 lb.
454 grammes = 1.0 lb.

Volume

1 Litre = 1.76 pints
4.55 litres = 1 gallon

Area

1 Hectare = 2.47 acres

Temperature

°F	32	40	50	60	70	75	85	95	105	140	175	212
°C	0	5	10	15	21	24	30	35	41	60	80	100

Celsius = 5/9 (Fahrenheit - 32)

Fahrenheit = 9/5 Celsius + 32

APPENDIX 2

ADDRESSES OF BEEKEEPING ORGANISATIONS

The British Beekeepers Association
National Agricultural Centre, Stoneleigh, Kenilworth, Warwickshire, CV8 2LZ

Welsh Beekeepers Association
P.A. Gregory Esq., Pentrebwlen, Llanddewi, Brefi, Tregaron, Dyfed

The Scottish Beekeepers Association
W.A. Mackenzie Esq., 9 Glenhome Avenue, Dyce, Aberdeen, AB2 OFF

Ulster Beekeepers Association
Charles Nicholson Esq., 57 Liberty Road, Carrickfergus, Co. Antrim, BT38 9DJ

The Federation of Irish Beekeepers Associations
Peter O'Reilly Esq., 11 Our Lady Place, Naas, Co. Kildare

Bee Farmers Association
B.A. Stenhouse Esq., Chelsea Cottage, Kennaways, Faversham, Kent, ME13 0AA
British Isles Bee Breeders Association
A. Knight Esq., 11 Thomson Drive, Codnor, DE5 9RU

International Bee Research Association
18, North Road, Cardiff, CF1 3DY

The National Honey Show
Rev. H.F. Capener, 1 Baldric Road, Folkestone, CT20 2NR

ADAS National Beekeeping Unit
National Beekeeping Specialist, Luddington E.H.S., Stratford-upon-Avon, CV37 9SJ

Bee Disease Insurance Ltd
M. Wakeman Esq., Lower Guytre Farm, Knighton, Powys, LD7 1UY

Central Association of Beekeepers
Mrs. M. English, 6 Oxford Road, Teddington, Middlesex, TW11 OPZ

APPENDIX 3

RECOMMENDED READING

Periodicals

'Bee Craft'
The official journal of the BBKA, published monthly
Secretary, 15 West Way, Copthorne Bank, Crawley, Sussex, RH10 3QS

'The British Bee Journal'
Published monthly.
British Bee Publications Ltd., 46 Queen Street, Geddington, Kettering, NN14 1AZ

'The Beekeepers Quarterly'
Northern Bee Books, Scout Bottom Farm, Mytholmroyd, Hebden Bridge, HX7 5JS

'Bee World'
Published quarterly
IBRA, 18 North Road, Cardiff, CF1 3DY

'The Scottish Beekeeper'
D. Blair Esq., 44 Dalhousie Road, Kilbarchan, PA10 2AT

'Welsh Bulletin'
Miss C. Exall, 14 Mumbles Road, Black Pill, Swansea

'Irish Beekeeper'
J.J. Doran Esq., St Judes, Mooncoin, Waterford

'*Gleanings in Bee Culture*'
American monthly
E.H. Thorne Ltd., Beehive Works, Wragby, Lincoln, LN3 5LA

'*American Bee Journal*'
Steele & Brodie Ltd., Newport on Tay, Wormit, Fife, Scotland.

Books

ABC and XYZ of Beekeeping - Roger Morse - **Root Co.**

A Case of Hives - Heath - **Bee Books New & Old**

All About Mead - Andrews - **Mills and Boon**

Anatomy & Dissection of the Honeybee - Dade - **IBRA**

Communication Among Social Bees - Lindauer - **Harvard Univ. Press**

Encyclopedia of Beekeeping - Morse & Hooper - **Blandford Press**

Honey: A Comprehensive Survey - Crane - **Heinemann**

Honeybee Biology - Free - **Central Association of Beekeepers**

Honeybee Ecology - Seeley - **Princeton University Press**

Honey Marketing - Riches - **Bee Books New & Old**

Honeybee Pathology - Bailey - **Academic Press**

Guide to Bees & Honey - Hooper - **Blandford Press**

The Behaviour & Social Life of Honeybees - Ribbands - **Dover Publications**

The Hive & the Honeybee - **Dadant & Sons**

The Pollination of Flowers - Proctor & Yeo - **Collins**

The World of the Honeybee - Butler - **Collins**

Insect Natural History - Imms - **Collins**

GLOSSARY

ALLERGIC REACTION
A reaction caused by a compound, usually protein, when it enters the body. Manifested by rashes, breathing difficulty, collapse.

AFB
American foul brood.

APHID
Small insect, Order Homoptera, which suck plant juices and secrete honeydew.

BACILLUS LARVAE
The causative organism of American Foul Brood.

BALLING
Workers clustering on a queen that they do not accept for some reason. Usually killing the queen.

BEE GLUE
Propolis.

BEE SPACE
Space around combs etc. which bees will leave unfilled. Usually $1/4$ to $3/8$".

BOTTLING TANK
Plastic or stainless steel tank from which honey is run into jars.

BRACE COMB
Pieces of comb built between the main combs, fixing them together.

BRAULA COECA	The bee louse. A small fly. Found mainly on Queens and Drones. Harmless, but larvae burrow in cappings and disfigure.
BROOD	Young developing bees in egg, larval and pupal stages, not yet emerged from cells.
BROOD CHAMBER	That part of hive used for brood rearing.
BROOD DISEASES	Diseases affecting brood i.e. AFB, EFB, Varroa, Sac brood, Chalk brood, Stone brood.
BROOD FOOD	Secretion of the glands of nurse bees which is fed to larvae. Sometimes called Bee Milk.
BROOD NEST	The comb space in the brood chamber occupied by brood.
CANDY	Fondant used for winter feed.
CAPPINGS	Thin wax covering over full honey cells Porous cappings used to cover brood cells.
CAST	A swarm with a virgin queen which leaves a colony after the prime swarm.
CELL	Hexagonal compartment of honeycomb.

CHALK BROOD Disease of larvae caused by fungus Ascosphaera apis.

CHILLED BROOD Larvae that have died from being too cold.

CLEANSING FLIGHT Flight of bees from hive after periods of confinement when they void faeces.

CLEARER BOARD Crown board fitted with bee escapes. Used for clearing bees from honey supers.

COLONY A community of bees on their combs but not including the hive.

COMB Wax structure of hexagonal cells built by bees in which they rear young and store honey and pollen.

CREAMED HONEY Old name for soft-set honey.

CROWN BOARD Inner cover to the hive, usually made of wood.

DEMAREE Name of beekeeper who devised method of swarm control by separating the queen from most of the brood.

DEXTROSE Another name for glucose.

DIASTASE Enzyme which coverts starch to maltose and dextrins.

DRIFTING	Bees returning to another colony in an apiary, rather than their own.
DRONE	Fertile male bee.
DRONE LAYER	Queen which lays unfertilized eggs which develop into drones.
DYSENTERY	Discharge of faeces within the hive.
EMERGE	The act of leaving the cell when a young bee is fully developed.
ENZYME	Catalysts produced by plants and animals to accelerate chemical reactions.
EFB	European foul brood.
FERMENTATION	Breakdown of sugars by yeasts.
FERTILE	Queen that has mated and produces worker brood. A sexually mature drone.
FONDANT	Soft sugar candy used for winter feed.
FORAGE	Wild and cultivated food sources of the bee.
FOULBROOD	American and European foul brood diseases.

FOUNDATION	Thin sheets of beeswax on which comb is built.
FRAME	Rectangular device of thin wood, sometimes plastic, for holding combs.
FRUCTOSE	A simple sugar found in honey.
HIVE	Home for bees provided by man.
HIVE TOOL	Metal implement designed for opening hives, separating combs etc.
HONEYDEW	Sweet liquid secreted by aphids. Collected by bees.
INVERT SUGAR	Mixture of glucose and fructose.
INVERTASE	An enzyme which converts sucrose to glucose and fructose.
IMAGO	Mature insect at time of emergence.
LARVA	Grub stage of developing bee. Unsealed brood.
LAEVULOSE	Fructose. Sometimes called Fruit Sugar.
LIFT	Portion of outer casing of double walled hive.
MEAD	Honey wine.
NECTAR	Sugary liquid secreted by flowers to attract insects and other pollinators.

NECTARY	Organ of plant which secretes nectar.
NOSEMA	Disease of adult bees caused by Nosema apis.
NUCLEUS	A small stock of bees with only a few combs.
PHEROMONE	A substance secreted by an animal to the outside which produces a response in other individuals of the same species.
PIPING	The noise made by a virgin queen, usually recently emerged.
POLLEN	Male element in sexual reproduction of plants. Produced on anthers. Essential bee food.
PROPOLIS	Resinous glue used by bees to seal hive etc.
PUPA	Third stage of developing bee when sealed in its cell.
QUEEN	A female bee, fully sexually developed.
QUEEN CELL	A cell in which a queen is reared.
QUEEN CUP	The start of a queen cell, resembling a shallow cup pointing downwards.

QUEEN EXCLUDER	A screen with openings of critical size which allows workers to pass through but not queens and drones.
RACK	Part of hive for honey storage. Synonymous with 'Super'.
ROYAL JELLY	Secretion of glands of nurse bees, used to feed larvae.
SAC BROOD	Virus disease of brood.
SECTION	Small bass wood or plastic frame 4 1/4 inch square used for comb honey production. Round sections are also available.
SKEP	Old fashioned beehive, dome shaped, made of straw, wicker etc.
SOLAR EXTRACTOR	Glass covered insulated box using the heat of the sun to render beeswax.
SPIRACLES	External openings of tracheae.
STOCK	A colony of bees with its hive.
SUCROSE	Cane or beet sugar.
SUPER	Part of hive above the brood chamber where honey is stored.
SUPERSEDURE	The natural replacement of an old queen by her daughter without swarming.

SWARM	Bees which have left their hive with a queen for the purpose of establishing a new colony.
THIXOTROPIC	A peculiarity of ling heather honey which jells in the comb and liquefies when agitated.
UNITING	Combining two or more colonies to form one large colony.
VARROASIS	Disease caused by the mite Varroa jacobsoni.
VEIL	Protective net that covers the head and neck.
VISCOSITY	The property of a liquid which controls the speed it flows etc.
WARMING CABINET	Insulated heated box for liquefying honey.
WAX	Secreted by worker bees for building comb.
WAX MOTH	A moth whose larvae destroy honeycomb.
WORKER	Female bee, not sexually developed.

INDEX

N

O

P

Q

R

S

T

U

V

W